MAKING THE WORLD LEGIBLE

In memory of Paul Marsh
(1952–2009)

'The increasing and almost universal hegemony of English makes the PEN Writers in Translation programme all the more necessary. The aptly titled *Making the World Legible* is a splendid venture, displaying as it does the richness and vitality of the work of so many international artists'
John Banville'

'This is a remarkable anthology of translations aided by the English PEN Writers in Translation scheme, every one of which feels in some way vital. Whether belonging to a nomadic Kazakh herdsman, a child soldier in Eritrea or an immigrant worker in Germany, these voices – some of them already brutally silenced – ring with the exhilarating authenticity of first-hand experience'
Adam Thorpe

'Writers in Translation is a powerful force for good in the world. As this fine anthology proves, good writing establishes distinct identities, while at the same time celebrating common humanity. It deserves a large and enthusiastic audience'
Andrew Motion

'This book opens many windows. English PEN has done us a service in supporting these translations'
James Buchan

'Rich in courage, eloquence and powerful indictment, a vibrant border-crossing revelation of contemporary international literature and an act of dialogue in itself, *Making the World Legible* is what writing is all about'
Ali Smith

'What a wonderful, and indispensable, project this is. All writing, anyway, emerges out of translation, and we are lost and impoverished without our umbilical connection with the world's literatures.'
Amit Chaudhuri

'Reading *Making the World Legible* was both chastening and inspiring: chastening because it reminded me how little I know about the non-anglophone literatures of this world, and inspiring because it reminded me how much literature there is out there in the world waiting to be found and read'
Carlo Gébler

MAKING
THE WORLD
LEGIBLE

Edited and with an introduction by
JULIAN EVANS

An anthology of writing from 5 years of
English PEN's Writers in Translation programme

English PEN's Writers in Translation programme is
supported by Bloomberg, and this anthology gratefully
acknowledges their assistance

10 9 8 7 6 5 4 3 2 1

English PEN exists to promote literature and its understanding,
to uphold writers' freedoms around the world, to campaign
against the persecution and imprisonment of writers for stating
their views, and to promote the friendly co-operation of writers
and free exchange of ideas. www.englishpen.org

The Reading Agency is an independent charity working
to inspire more people to read more. It has close links with the
public library service, and also works with schools,
adult learning providers, prisons, workplaces, publishers,
broadcasters, and others. Please visit:
www.readingagency.org.uk for more information

A CIP catalogue record for this book is available from
the British Library

ISBN 978-0-9564806-2-0

First Published in 2010

Typefaces used. Headers set in 10/12pt Neuzeit S. Published
by Linotype, 1966. Text set in 9/12pt Archer. Published by
Hoefler & Frere-Jones, 2001.

Printed and bound by CPIMackays, Chatham ME5 8TD

Designed by **here**, Temple Works, Brett Road,
London E8 1JR www.heredesign.co.uk

Contents

Introduction

In the early 1990s, when Russia was holed and cracking under the stress of capitalism's arrival, I stood in the snow outside a brown, two-storey frame house on a village road about 30km from Moscow. The village was Peredelkino, the dacha was Boris Pasternak's (it was now a museum). Inside, the furnishings were spartan, and the writer's large writing room on the first floor contained, as it had done when he was alive, only a table, chair, and bookshelves. In an odd shift of temporal perspective, its windows looked out over a snowy hill crowned with a little Orthodox cemetery, hugged tight by close-planted firs, where he was buried.

The impact of the house and place, the austere arrangements (Pasternak never acquired a telephone) and the eerie landscape, was jolting, like being dropped into a closed world where only the the labours of creation counted. Those who met Pasternak tended to talk about him as a 'cloud-dweller' – Stalin called him that – or a holy fool. In 1960 the writer Olga Andreev Carlisle, who had interviewed him for the *Paris Review*, wrote of the similarity of his speech to his poetry and of finding 'something a little strange and forbidding in [his] youthfulness [Pasternak was seventy] as if something – was it art? – had mixed itself with the very substance of the man to preserve him'.

Pasternak's poetry, not *Doctor Zhivago*, is what he is best remembered for in Russia: his poetry and his translations of Goethe and Shakespeare. But Pasternak distrusted translation. He disliked the translations of *Zhivago* that made him world-famous, though he didn't blame the translators who, he felt, had been used 'like translators everywhere' to reproduce a literal version rather than the tone of what he had written. His feelings about translation, and literature, also had a reactionary element. He told Olga Carlisle that 'the only interesting sort of translation is that of classics... As far as modern writing is concerned, it is rarely rewarding to translate it, although it might be easy.' He likened the activity to 'copying paintings'. 'Imagine yourself copying a Malevich; wouldn't it be boring?'

He may have been influenced by his task at hand, which was to translate the prolific, possibly sub-Malevich Czech surrealist Vítězslav Nezval. But Pasternak's is a not uncommon resistance. Dr Johnson believed 'Poetry cannot be translated'; the critic George Steiner has said that we cannot see Pushkin's greatness unless we know Russian, and there is no forgetting Robert Frost's definition that 'Poetry is what gets lost in translation'. What is noticeable among writers and critics is an ambivalence about translation, a grudgingness, a dismissiveness that often goes with a tendency to exploitation, or at least to serving their interests. Pasternak occupied himself with translations both to supplement his income from writing, and to stay out of trouble when the purges of Soviet intellectuals started up again in 1936. Proust translated Ruskin into French as a literary exercise and part of his aesthetic apprenticeship, and Paul Auster translated contemporary French poets as 'a way to earn money, pay for food and put bread on the table'. Milan Kundera is known to be highly attentive to his translations and to his translators – so long as they accept that their versions are subject to the 'supreme authority' of his style.

None of this is very objectionable. Pasternak, were he alive today, might acknowledge that his reputation in half the world rests on his translations, and that he might be wrong about modern writing. Proust deeply admired Ruskin and recognised that he owed a layer of his style to having learned how to position himself between the French language's fluidity and Ruskin's impatient sentences: 'you know with what a scrupulous hand – but a pious one too and as gentle as I was able – I approached it,' he wrote to Georges Goyau. But there still remains a widespread feeling that both translated literary work, and the process of translation, are not quite writing, not quite art in the exclusive, Pasternakian sense. They are, to borrow the writer George Borrow, 'at best an echo'.

About three decades ago, British readers were going through an era of anglophone obeisance that was both political and literary. The habit of focus on Europe, the primacy of Sartre and Camus, of Böll and Moravia and Montale, of Robbe-Grillet, Duras, Sarraute, Handke, Andersch, Bachmann, Sciascia, Pavese, had faded: instead we were reading De Lillo, Heller, McCarthy, Morrison, Pynchon, Roth, Updike. We were reading García Márquez too, who, with *One Hundred Years of Solitude*, singlehandedly sparked an American era of translation that also brought us the vividities of Cabrera Infante, Cortázar, Fuentes, Vargas Llosa. The translation of Europe did not quite stop – there were still Grass and Kundera and Calvino and Levi, and Michael Hofmann's and others' brilliant revivals of Joseph Roth – but the ball didn't look like rolling back until the publication in 1986 of a novel about an (as it were symbolically) unloved outsider, Jean-Baptiste Grenouille. Even so, efforts to replicate the runaway success of Patrick Süskind's *Perfume* – Christoph Ransmayr's *Die Letzte Welt* (*The*

Last World) was one try at it – failed.

Ransmayr's novel failed not because it was poor. It wasn't, it was an accomplished and often brilliant retelling of Ovid. But it failed because, once again, translation was seen as an adjunct, a minor activity. The guiding idea in British publishers' and readers' minds was that in order for a book written in another language to sell and be read in the British market, a kind of makeover had to be perpetrated that turned it into a) a bestseller and b) *a British book by a British writer*: a book almost purged of foreignness, whose qualities were those of an English novel shaded with tinges of exoticism. Factor into those requirements the cost of translation, and publishers were only ready to translate books they felt like hyping.

If we accept this significant structural defect in British publishing, the argument stops being about why balls roll in particular directions, and becomes about narrowness. There is no doubt that Margaret Thatcher and Ronald Reagan encouraged a generation of anglophone insularity and isolationism. But that it lasted as long as it did is because as readers we too were a bit like Pasternak, existing inside a snug anglophone bubble. Islands are traps, as Bruce Chatwin once noted, and so are continents that believe too heartily in their hegemony. To escape must imply, sooner or later, a meeting and an accommodation with the *outremer*, abroad – with otherness – that may be inconvenient and even disturbing.

What did this bubble of the 1980s and 1990s feel like? Obviously translations were neither censored nor banned. We were even blessed by the occasional narrow fashion, such as the rediscovery of Danilo Kiš and other 'Balkan' writers when the Yugoslav wars broke out in 1991. Translation went on uninterrupted in committed places: at exemplary publishers like Harvill and Quartet and the imprints of some university presses. In 1989 the British Centre for Literary Translation was founded at the University of East Anglia by W G Sebald.

Yet the choice of languages in which literary work of value was thought to exist confirmed our narrowness and made those years, I think, complacent and constricting: Spanish, Portuguese, French, German – the club of imperial languages – with a bit of Italian, Russian, Dutch and Scandinavian thrown in. No Arabic, Persian, Turkish, Chinese, Dravidian or Indo-Aryan languages to speak of. Barely a minority language in sight. From within our bubble we were pleased at the renewal of English by the 'Commonwealth' generation writing from or informed by India, Pakistan, Sri Lanka, the Caribbean. If Vikram Seth had written his novel *A Suitable Boy* in Hindi, or Arundhati Roy *The God Of Small Things* in Malayalam, there would have been no such renewal. Plus it is easy to guess what those books' impact in the anglophone world might have been.

What is my point? It's in another question, which is: what, exactly, are the benefits of quitting the bubble, and meeting otherness? Put it another way, what is so good about translation? It brings 'foreign' writers closer. But what's the good of that proximity? Well, Pushkin had a lovely expression for translators: he called them 'the post-horses of literature'. Staying with just the Russians for a moment, what have we not revelled in, and understood, from our messengered versions of Tolstoy and Dostoyevsky, Bulgakov, Chekhov, Akhmatova, Pasternak, Pelevin? 'Literature', dusty with age, is other things beneath the dust: a window, a picture, a territory viewed for the first time, a wall looked over or graffitied on, a vantage point gazed or taken aim from; a discovery. Not in the orientalist, tourist sense, but in the sense of a discovery that leads back to a re-discovery of ourselves. To make a discovery of something other than us, that is nevertheless human, is to read ourselves with more clarity.

Translation rests on an insistence: that we seek the individual in the communal, the communal in the individual. It is an extension, not an adjunct of literature's account of all our variousness, possibility, complexity, and continuity. Any literary work made anywhere is a request from writer to reader: Do you recognise anything? Are we both human beings? 'Believe in me,' Don Quixote says. And we do. It doesn't really matter how many people speak the language in which a writer writes. (Yes, languages struggle to survive, and that is definitely another argument.) What matters is how charged with meaning the words and images are in the original, and their communicability to the reader when they are translated. The best novels are as much written by the reader as the writer.

So no, translation is not an adjunct, or something less than writing. Umberto Eco, asked which language could be called Europe's, answered that translation was the language of Europe. We could extend his answer. Translation is the world's language. There are pitfalls, as with most definitions. A world in which translation, its sales and royalties and popularity, becomes big business is a place in which the ultimate flattening of localness will be as big a risk as it might be in a world ruled by global English. And those writers who set out to extend their ambitions into as many other languages as possible, expanding their market and increasing their income (who can blame them?), are at an equal risk of establishing a category of international-lite literature. The novelist Tim Parks, admirably oppositional, has detected the atopian absurdities in Kazuo Ishiguro's declared 'need to write an English that is easily translatable, the better to reach out to the whole world' and in the habit of Scandinavian writers to choose the names of their characters with foreign readers in mind. We need to feel the commonality of our fate, to see that the others are us and we are the others. But unless we feel our specificity too, we're likely to end up living in the cultural equivalent of an airport. You have to root yourself in the local in order to reach the 'universal.

Perhaps because the world began to twist and turn after 1989, and change began to drift in on the air, we are at last more conscious that there is a world beyond our island and its mothership across the Atlantic. Perhaps the wars of the last decade – Iraq, Afghanistan, Palestine – have made us realign and retreat from that hegemony. Perhaps we noticed in the process that other languages' and cultures' stories were at least as interesting as ours. Perhaps the global mall in which today every commodity is available – cheap travel, consumable experience, multiculturalism, all shades of terrorism, even the exchange of ideas – has made us more curious.

When the English PEN Writers in Translation programme was formally set up in late 2004, it was the brainchild of several people, not least Susie Nicklin, director of English PEN and wife of Paul Marsh, to whose memory this book is dedicated. Its committee's most important early decision was to capitalise on that supposed curiosity. It was an aim in keeping with both PEN's current aspirations and its founding principles, established when the original PEN Club was set up in 1921, in the wake of war, to promote literature as a bridge to greater understanding between nations and cultures. There are now 144 PEN centres in more than one hundred countries across the planet.

The belief that literature knows no frontiers, and that freedom of expression is a fundamental right, are central to PEN's charter, and it's under those banners that Writers in Translation advances. Its committee of literary translators, writers, agents and publishers, reading widely and meeting two or three times a year, believed from the start that curiosity needs to be fed. Beyond the principle of championing literature in translation, there was a practical need for individual books to be concretely helped. Without that help, there was always a good chance they would sink unremarked, their authors' foreignness and their publishers' limited resources (all funds and energy spent on the translation itself before the book had even left the warehouse) dooming them to silence.

Since that time, thanks to the news organisation Bloomberg and

Arts Council England, Writers in Translation has given awards to help promote thirty-six translated books to date: fiction, non-fiction and poetry. By making it a condition of an award that the publisher should include public events in their promotion of the work, Writers in Translation has also helped bring writers and translators to the UK and host events where the public can meet authors and have their curiosity about authors turned into curiosity to read. Over only half a decade we have seen an increase in the number of public events featuring international authors, initiating a virtuous circle, bringing work to wider attention from readers, critics and the media, encouraging publishers to take more imaginative decisions in their commissioning. It has been rewarding to see more writing in translation included in bookseller's promotions, especially when produced by small independent publishers. The awards granted by WiT can make a very significant difference when spent creatively by publishers who are passionate about international writing.

And so to this book. If there is still any doubt that translation is the world's language, the thirty-six extracts printed here make the case better than any argument. At the inaugural meeting of the committee, when the first books were submitted, we gave that original award unanimously to Anna Politkovskaya's *Putin's Russia*. It is a book of great, even immoderate passion; it had an extra distinction, of being banned on Politkovskaya's home territory, her unsparing dissection of corruption, cronyism, violence, illegality and fraud being too much for its president and his associates to stomach. Her target is injustice, high or low. In 'Old ladies and new Russians', extracted here, she gives a sketch of what its lawless economics mean for ordinary Russians living in Moscow province, at a village where wealthy outsiders have seized a nature reserve to build themselves grandiose dachas. It's a picture that tells me more about Russia than any amount of BBC commentary on Putin's activities inside the Kremlin. (And mirrors a myriad situations like it. Something similarly wretched, I have heard, has happened next to the writer's village at Peredelkino.)

It's easy, possibly lazy, to wrap up an era in an arbitrarily selected event. But let us look for a moment at the variousness and quality of some of the work that has appeared in English translation since *Putin's Russia* was published – going on to sell more than 25,000 copies and to be distributed clandestinely and courageously in Russia. Nasrin Alavi's *We Are Iran*, another investigation into life at the level of the ordinary citizen, collected the work of Iranian bloggers – an impressively technically advanced, gender-neutral group – to assemble a picture of a country in which leaders and people are even more disconnected. It's both fascinating and shaming (because you feel you should have known) to be informed that the veil was first used by rich Muslims as a status symbol, and that the Koranic instruction for women 'not to show off their adornment except only that which is apparent and to draw their veils all over their bosoms' was only later interpreted to mean hair, neck and ears.

From further east, Mukhamet Shayakhmetov's *The Silent Steppe* recalled the end of a nomadic Kazakh culture, victim of another swooping and irreversible oppression; from Africa, Jean Hatzfeld's *Into The Quick of Life*, a work of witness that collected oral histories by victims of the Rwandan genocide, personalised that people's tragedy as revealingly as another eyewitness account, the diary of a young Viennese Jew named Ruth Maier, personalised the murderous reach of the Holocaust. (Maier emigrated to Norway after the Austrian *Anschluss* and then, after Germany invaded Norway, was deported to Auschwitz and gassed at the age of 22. There is nothing to make headlines in her sometimes earnest, sometimes frivolous, often not well behaved chronicle of a girl's adolescence and young woman's education into adulthood, love and disappointment that never quenches hope. But is it possible to fall a little in love with a dead woman? A jumping spark of connectedness, of being permanently plugged into the mains of life and humanity, keeps her artless testimony vividly alive although she died almost seventy years ago, and her *Diary* absolutely reset my historical and emotional compass as I read it.)

Something personal – but a million miles from the luxury of the misery memoir – has characterised much documentary and non-fiction writing in translation over the last five years. Experience cannot be replicated, it seems to say, but it can be translated. Even Samir Kassir's *Being Arab*, a fluently savage polemic about the Arab world's stagnation and failure to come to terms with its own modernity, was as personal as it could be. As John Pilger noted, Samir could have been kinder to himself; and if he had been he might not have been assassinated by a car bomb in 2005. Anna Politkovskaya might not have been murdered either, outside her Moscow apartment a year later, if she had been kinder to those she tormented with the truth. Neither's killers have been found – leading to the dim but inescapable reflection that those most acutely aware of the need for open debate and humane discourse are always less well protected than those wanting to silence them.

'It is the story-teller's task to elicit sympathy and a measure of understanding for those who lie outside the boundaries of state approval,'

Graham Greene wrote. In the last five years too a more than representative cross-section of fiction and poetry that answers that description has been translated from the Albanian, Croatian, Slovak, Polish, Russian, Turkish and Hebrew, as well as the usual French, German, Portuguese and Spanish. (It's worth noting that significant numbers of those writing in Europe's 'big' languages now do so as migrants, exiles and refugees.) This is a remarkable shift: the rare-as-hen's-teeth novel translated from Arabic, for example, an almost unprecedented sight in Britain, has given way to a steady flow of writing from the Near East and western Asia.

A stunning fecundity, in fact, has come to light that is almost worrisome: what if these writers eclipse English novelists in the richness of their tapestries? Literature, of course, is the self-repairing rug par excellence, a constant busy (sometimes fussy and self-absorbed) pattern-making against the meaningless shapes and noise of greater mundane life. It belongs to no country but the republic of letters; to Milan Kundera's basic question, 'what is existence?', there are English as there are Colombian or Ivorian or French or Kazakh answers. The only stipulation is one of common value, and the possibility of revision of *our* answers through others'.

Reporting, shaping, lighting, expediting, detonating those answers with brilliance and significance: it has been done in satire (Peter Pišťanek's demented *Rivers of Babylon* trilogy comes to mind); in tragicomedy (Dubravka Ugresic's *The Ministry of Pain* and Ahmadou Kourouma's pugnacious *Allah Is Not Obliged*); through memorialising (Evelio Rosero's deceptive *The Armies*, Ron Leshem's rough and randy *Beaufort*, Eli Amir's acutely moving *The Dove Flyer*, Elias Khoury's magnificent *Gate of the Sun*) and absurdist memoir (Fatos Kongoli's irresistible *The Loser*); with compact intensity (Atiq Rahimi's *The Patience Stone*, Alberto Méndez' *Blind Sunflowers* and Hassan Blasim's *The Madman of Freedom Square*) and leisurely expansiveness (Saša Stanišić's *How the Soldier Repairs the Gramophone*, Alaa Al-Aswany's *The Yacoubian Building*); in slang (Faïza Guène's *Dreams From the Endz*) and poetry (Soleïman Adel Guémar's rawly beautiful *State of Emergency*). Whether the voices are those of an unemployed migrant teenager, a retired teacher with an eye for his naked neighbour, an Israeli conscript or an Afghan wife, through translation we perceive that the predicament of each hovers around a feeling of both completion and deprivation, that they – and we – have come into being as humans in a space that lies exactly between freedom and its loss; exactly as Anna Akhmatova expressed it in a poem written in 1915, translated by

Peter Norman:

> We thought we were beggars, and possessed nothing at all,
> But when we began to lose one thing, then another,
> So that each day turned into
> One of remembrance –
> We began to compose songs
> About God's great generosity,
> And about our former great wealth.

It has been done, above all, in translation. A few further words on that: another Russian, Yevgeny Yevtushenko, whom Robert Frost admired (and, one imagines, read in English), admitted the possibility of translation but with an old-world charm noted that 'Translation is like a woman. If it is beautiful, it is not faithful. If it is faithful, it is most certainly not beautiful.' The translator Edith Grossman, excellent re-maker of the English *Don Quixote*, agreed with Yevtushenko in a roundabout way a few years ago, saying that 'Fidelity is our noble purpose, but it does not have much, if anything, to do with what is called literal meaning. A translation can be faithful to tone and intention, to meaning. It can rarely be faithful to words or syntax, for these are peculiar to specific languages and are not transferable.' This, I think, is a given among literary translators today, who are writers as well as linguists. It is certainly true of all the translators here.

I talked about the self-repairing rug of literature, and for any one language it is self-evidently the translations of other languages into that language that join the pieces together. We could talk long into the night about the practical drawbacks to the situation of literary translation today (insufficient, inattentive to minority languages, ill paid) or the more metaphysical, Pasternakian drawbacks to translation as expression. But one thing is sure: the richer the rug, the more various the pattern-making, the more interesting that literature becomes. No longer the preserve of the wealthy languages – thank heavens – or the western or the post-imperial or the most cocky languages, it belongs to a world demos. Its language, translation, has only one job: to make the world legible. As long it does that, it hardly matters where its answers come from.

—

Julian Evans (Chair, Writers in Translation)

Old ladies and new Russians

Two old ladies, Maria Savina, a former champion milkmaid, and Zinaida Fenoshina, a former equally champion cowherd, stand in the middle of the forest, angrily shaking upraised sticks in the direction of a bulldozer. It is roaring away at full throttle, and they are shouting as loudly as they can for all to hear: 'Be off! Away with you! How much longer must we put up with this sort of thing?'

From behind ancient trees, surly security guards appear and surround them as if to say, 'Leave now while you still can, or we shoot.'

Nikolai Abramov – a retired vet, the village elder and the organiser of the demonstration – spreads his arms. 'They want to drive us off our own land. We shall defend it to the death. What else is left?'

The theatre of operations is on the outskirts of the village of Pervomaiskoe in the Narofomin District of Moscow Province. The epicentre is the grounds of an old estate formerly owned by the Berg family. It dates from 1904 and is today protected by the State as a natural and cultural heritage site.

When they have calmed down a little, the old people shake their heads sadly. 'There, in our old age we've joined the Greens. What else can we do? There's only us to defend our park from this scum. Nobody else is going to.'

The scum are New Russians who have hired soulless barbarian developers to erect 34 houses right in the middle of the century-old Berg Park. Maria and Zinaida are members of a special ecological group created by the village assembly of Pervomaiskoe to organise direct action against the despoilers of the environment.

Paying little attention to the Green activists, the trucks continue to drive and the tractors to roar among the precious ancient trees. After an hour's work they have cut a swathe through the woodlands. This is to be the central 'avenue' of the future cottage settlement. Pipes, reinforcement wire and concrete slabs lie all over the place. The building work is in full swing and really is being carried out as if to maximise damage to the natural environment. Already 130 cubic metres of timber have been taken as rare species were felled. Wherever you look there are notches on cedars and firs, marking them for slaughter. The machinery brazenly wrecks the environment, churning up layers of clay from the depths and pitilessly burying deep beneath it the ecosystem of the forest floor which has formed over the years.

'Have you heard of the Weymouth Pine?' Tatyana Dudenus asks. She is head of the ecological group and a research associate at one of the region's medical institutes. 'We had five specimens growing in the grounds of our heritage park. They were the only ones in the whole of Moscow Province. The Bergs made a hobby of propagating rare tree species. Three of these Weymouth Pines have now been sawn down for no better reason than that the developers wanted to run a street for their new estate just where they were growing. Other precious species are under threat: the Siberian Silver Fir and Larch, the White Poplar, a White Cedar, *Thuja occidentalis*, the only specimen in Moscow Province. In just the last three days we have lost more than 60 trees. It wouldn't be so bad if they were destroying the less outstanding or sickly specimens, but they have quite a different approach. They decide where they want to construct a road and cut down anything that's in the way. They decide where they want to put up a cottage and clear the site, taking no account of the rarity of the trees they are destroying. The forest here is legally classified as Grade One, which means it is against the law to touch these trees. In order to obtain permission to fell them you have to demonstrate 'exceptional circumstances' and support your application with a recommendation from the State Ecological Inspectorate. For every such hectare you need the express permission of the Federal government.'

When the fate of Berg Park was being decided, none of this was done. The Pervomaiskoe Greens lodged writs with the Narofomin court to bring the brazen *nouveaux riches* into line. They petitioned Judge Yelena Golubeva, who had been assigned the case, for an injunction to halt the building work until the hearing, since otherwise, after the trees had been felled, a verdict in their favour would be of little use.

However, this is the age of the oligarchs in Russia. Every branch of government understands only the language of their rustling banknotes. Judge Golubeva did not even consider granting an injunction to halt the construction work and, when it was already in progress, deliberately failed to conduct a hearing.

Nearly all those unique trees were felled.

Valerii Kulakovsky emerges from the posse of guards. He is the deputy director of the Promzhilstroy Company, which calls itself a cooperative of home builders. Kulakovsky advises me to stay out of this. He says some extremely influential people in Moscow have an interest in the estate: they are going to live here. This is soon confirmed. I discover that the 'cooperative' has managed to acquire property rights over the Berg hectares, which according to the law are the property of the nation. This is totally illegal. Kulakovsky just shrugs and tries to explain his own position. 'We are very tired of these endless demonstrations by the villagers. What do you expect me to do now, when I have put so much money into this, bought the land, started building? Who do you think is going to give it all back to me?'

He also says they have no plans to back down.

They did not back down. Berg Park ceased to exist. The felling of our finest forests in the interests of the oligarchs and their companies is going on throughout the land.

Not long before the Green old ladies of Pervomaiskoe mounted the desperate defence of their ancient park, the Supreme Court of Russia considered the same matter of principle as it applied to Russia as a whole. The case was known as the 'Forest Issue'.

'Bear in mind the interests of the property owners. They have acquired the land, built the houses, and now you want to turn everything back.' The lawyer in the Supreme Court repeated what Kulakovsky had said almost word for word.

The ecologist lawyers Olga Alexeeva and Vera Mishchenko, who were defending the interests of society as a whole against the caprices of New Russians, had a different take on the matter: 'Every citizen of this country has the right to life and enjoyment of the national heritage. If we are truly citizens of Russia, then it is our duty to ensure that future generations receive no less a national heritage than today's generations enjoy. In any case, how can we take seriously property rights which have been acquired illegally?'

The essence of the 'Forest Issue' was that Russian ecologists, under the leadership of the Moscow Institute of Ecological Legal Issues, Eco-Juris, which brought the case, emanded the repeal of twenty-two orders of the Cabinet of Ministers transferring Grade One forests to the category of non-afforested land. This permitted the felling of more than 34, 000 hectares of prime forest in Russia.

Russia's forests are divided into three categories. Grade One relates to those deemed particularly important either for society or for the natural environment. These are forests containing highly valued species, habitats of rare birds and animals, reservations and parks, and urban and suburban Green Belts. The Forestry Code of the Russian Federation accordingly recognises Grade One forests as part of the national heritage. Berg Park came into this category.

The formal applicant for this change of categories and subsequent right to fell trees was, oddly enough, the Forestry Commission of the

Russian Federation, Rosleskhoz. It is the body which has the right to submit documents relating to the legal status of forests for signature by the Prime Minister. The 22 orders disputed by the ecologists had been made without the statutory State ecological inspection, with the result that the national heritage became the prey of short-term interests. Where forests were cut down they were replaced by petrol stations, garages, industrial estates, local wholesale markets, domestic waste dumps and, of course, housing estates.

The ecologists consider this last option to be the least objectionable, but only providing the new house owners behave responsibly towards the magnificent forests surrounding their houses and do not destroy their roots in the course of laying drainage systems.

While the 'Forest Issue' was being considered and the judges were taking their time, almost another 950 hectares of top-quality forests were condemned to destruction under new orders signed by the Prime Minister. The greatest damage was done in the Khanty-Mansiisk and Yamalo-Nenetsk autonomous regions, where trees were destroyed for the benefit of oil and gas companies. Moscow Province also suffered: what happened to Berg Park was the result of deliberate judicial procrastination.

While the paperwork was being taken care of and nobody had the courage to dot the legal 'i's or cross the legal 't's, the struggle for the forest in Pervomaiskoe became violent. When, at the request of the prosecutor's office, the ecological group went to record the barbaric results of the developers' activities with a videocamera, police reinforcements were brought in. A fight broke out, the camera was broken and the ecologists, all of them elderly people, were beaten up.

'Of course, we do not want to wage a war, but we have been left with no option,' Nikolai Abramov, the village elder, says by way of explanation. 'The estate was the last place in the village where we could go to walk. There were usually old people and mothers with prams there. There is a school for 300 pupils and a kindergarten in the grounds. All the rest has been developed with cottages for the New Russians.'

The veteran ecologists are aware that they are at war primarily with the super-rich, people who command amounts of money the like of which they themselves have never seen. They have heard it talk, however. At a village assembly, Alexander Zakharov, chairman of the Pervomaiskoe Rural District Council, openly declared that the sums of money involved were too great for there to be any possibility of reversing the situation. Here is what Igor Kulikov, chairman of the Ecological Union of Moscow Province, wrote to the provincial prosecutor, Mikhail Avdyukov: 'The chairman of the council publicly stated to members of the ecological group elected by the assembly that he had given their names and addresses to the Mafia, which would deal with them if they did not stop their protests.'

Alexander Zakharov is undoubtedly one of the central characters in this unseemly tale. If he had stood firm, not one dacha would have encroached on the grounds of the Berg Park. At the foot of the documents that ultimately permitted the felling of the Pervomaiskoe trees, in contravention of the law and against the resolution of the village assembly, is Zakharov's signature.

There is not much wrong with our laws in Russia. It is just that not many people want to obey them.

—

From *Putin's Russia* by **Anna Politkovskaya**, translated from the Russian by Arch Tait (The Harvill Press 2004)

Anna Politkovskaya's *Putin's Russia*, published in the winter of 2004, was the first book to receive a Writers in Translation award. Banned in Russia, it has gone on to sell more than 25,000 copies in Britain. The book is not simply a biography or analysis of Putin's presidency, but a biopsy of a Russia suffering chronically from the corruption, cronyism and cynical destruction of its civil society that has occurred under his leadership.

Known to many as 'Russia's lost moral conscience', **Anna Politkovskaya** was shot and murdered outside her flat in Moscow in October 2006. Few doubt that her killing was in reprisal for her reporting. She was a special correspondent for the Russian newspaper *Novaya Gazeta* and the recipient of many honours for her writing.

Arch Tait studied Russian at Cambridge and Moscow State University. He began translating in 1986 after a meeting with Valentina Jacques, then editor of the magazine *Soviet Literature*, and from 1993 he was the UK editor of the *Glas New Russian Writing* translation series. To date he has translated seventeen books and more than thirty stories by most of the leading Russian writers of today.

The Ministry of Pain

They called me Professor Lucić at first, but once we'd settled into our topic for the first semester they switched to Comrade, 'drugarice', affectedly drawing out the final e and raising it at the end like a verbal tail. The word 'comrade' became a kind of intimate password between my new students and me, linking us, one and all, to the school benches we had long since abandoned, to times long past and a country no longer in existence: 'comrade' was the word used by Yugoslav children in the fifties and early sixties to address their teachers. Here in Holland it was not so much a word as the tinkle of a Pavlovian bell. And although I addressed them with the formal 'you', I referred to them as my 'pupils' or 'kids'. It was all a humorous bit of make-believe: I wasn't and never had been anybody's 'comrade'; they weren't pupils. Nor were they kids, most of them ranging between twenty and thirty, which made me only a few years older. Meliha was my age, and Johanneke and Laki were older than I was. The only thing reminiscent of the rules of the game, therefore, was my use of the formal 'you'.

They'd come with the war. Some had acquired refugee status, others had not. Most of the guys, the ones from Serbia and Croatia, had left to avoid military service; some had come from the war zones; others had gone along for the ride and stayed on. There were also those who had heard that the Dutch authorities were generous with welfare and accommodations for Yugoslav refugees and came to exchange the dicey currency of their lives for the hard stuff. And there were those who had happened upon Dutch partners.

Mario had met a Dutch girl in Austria – where his parents had sent him, fearing he'd be conscripted into the Croatian Army – and she took him back to Holland with her. 'Maybe I married her for the passport and fell in love with her after the fact,' he once told me with a smile. 'Or maybe I was in love with her to begin with and made it official because of the passport. I can't remember.'

Boban had gone to India on a package deal with a group of Belgrade matrons, followers of Sai Baba. The trip had been engineered and financed by his mother, whose only concern was to save him temporarily from the army. In India he'd ditched the tour and wandered about for two months, but then he picked up dysentery and boarded the first plane out. He landed in Amsterdam, where he was to change planes for Belgrade, but somewhere on the way from one loo to another in Schipol he'd had a brilliant epiphany and asked for political asylum. It was still a possibility back then. For a year or two the Dutch authorities were lenient: anyone coming from the former Yugoslavia could use the war as a credible motivation. But in time things changed and the gate slammed shut.

Johanneke was Dutch. She spoke 'our language' fluently and with a Bosnian accent. Her parents were Dutch leftists who had built roads and railway tracks with international youth brigades after World War II. Later they went to the Dalmatian coast as tourists. During one of their stays Johanneke visited Sarajevo, fell in love with a Bosnian and was stranded there for a while. Now, divorced and the mother of two little girls, she had made up her mind to get a degree in Slavonic languages. She was an accredited court interpreter from 'our language' to Dutch, which turned out to be highly useful: she would translate and authenticate any document our kids needed.

There were those who showed up once or twice and quietly disappeared. Laki was from Zagreb. He remained in my memory because he was the only one who called me Mrs: Mrs Lucić. He clearly considered 'comrade' to be 'Yugoslav', 'Communist', and therefore 'anti-Croat'. He had a Zagreb way of talking that got on my nerves – the la-di-da stress on the last syllable, the constant use of reflexives, verbal forms referring to the self, that made him sound intimately related to everything on earth. Like so many others Laki had come to Amsterdam for the cheap pot. He had come before the war and studied Slavonic languages and literatures for years, living on welfare and in heavily subsidized public housing. The kids all said that he was a paid police informer, that he bragged about translating the bugged telephone conversations between Yugoslav mafia members the Dutch police had under surveillance. The kids called him Laki the Linguist because he claimed to be working on a Dutch-Croatian dictionary for which he could never find a grant. He refused to acknowledge the existing Dutch–Serbo-Croatian dictionary.

Then there was Zole, who had set up house with a Dutch gay partner to qualify for a residence permit, and Darko, from Opatija, who really was gay. The Dutch authorities were particularly generous about granting asylum to those who claimed they had been discriminated against in their home countries for 'sexual difference', more generous than to the war's rape victims. As soon as word got round, people climbed on the bandwagon in droves. The war was a fig leaf for everything. It was something like the national lottery: while many tried their luck out of genuine misfortune, others did it simply because the opportunity presented itself. And under such aberrant circumstances winners and losers had to be judged by new criteria.

They studied Servo-Kroatisch because it was easy. If you didn't have a refugee visa, you could prolong your stay legally by enrolling in a university programme. Some had begun or even completed programmes at home, but they meant next to nothing here. Servo-Kroatisch was the fastest and easiest way to come by a Dutch diploma, not that even a Dutch diploma would get you very far. If, like Ana, you had another language as your 'major', you could pick up a few effortless credits with Servo-Kroatisch, but if what you were really after was student loans and scholarships, then Servo-Kroatisch was your ticket.

They coped. Most of them 'played tennis'. Playing tennis in their group slang meant house-cleaning. It paid 15 guilders an hour. Some worked as dishwashers or waiters in restaurants. Ante picked up small change playing the accordion in the Noordermarkt. Ana sorted mail in the post office every morning. 'It's not so bad,' she would say. 'I feel like the dwarf in Čapek's *Postman's Tale.*'

But the best paying job you could get without a work permit was a job at the 'Ministry'. One of 'our people' found work at a place where they made clothes for sex shops and soon the whole gang was working there. It wasn't strenuous: all you had to do was assemble items of sadomasochist clothing out of leather, rubber and plastic. Three times a week Igor, Nevena and Selim went to Regulateurstraat in Amsterdam Nord where the Atelier Demask, purveyor to the many-faceted Dutch porno industry, was located. There was an S/M porno club in The Hague called The Ministry of Pain, and my students took to calling their porno sweat shop the 'Ministry'. 'Those S/M types, Comrade, they're real snappy dressers,' Igor would joke. 'They don't think the most beautiful body is a naked body. I wouldn't forget that if I were a Gucci or Armani.'

The kids did a good job of coping – considering where they came from. They dragged their former country behind them like a train. People said the Yugomafia was responsible for a third of the criminal activities in Amsterdam. The papers were full of its thefts, prostitute trafficking, black marketeering, murders and vendettas.

Nor did they know what to make of the country's current status. If they mentioned Croatia and Bosnia, it was with great caution. If they mentioned Yugoslavia, which was now the name for Serbia and Montenegro, it was with great agony. They couldn't deal with the names the media kept throwing out. Rump Yugoslavia, for instance. ('Where'd they get that one from, for Christ's sake?' Meliha would cry. 'Is it because they hacked it up like a steak?') Yugoslavia, the country where they'd been born, where they'd come from, no longer existed. They did their best to deal with it by steering clear of the name, shortening it to Yuga (as the Gastarbeiter, the migrant workers in Germany, had done before them) and thus 'the former Yugoslavia' to 'the former Yuga' or playfully transforming it into Titoland or The Titanic. As for its inhabitants, they became Yugos or, more often, simply 'our people'. The possessive pronoun also came in handy when referring to the language they spoke together (none of them being Slovenian, Macedonian or Albanian): to avoid its former, now politically incorrect name of Serbo-Croatian, they called it simply 'our language'.

—

From *The Ministry of Pain* by **Dubravka Ugresic**, translated from the Croatian by Michael Henry Heim (Saqi 2005)

The Ministry of Pain is a black comedy of displacement and reinvention about a group of refugees from the Balkan wars of the 1990s. Washed up on the shoals of liberal Holland, they take shelter in Amsterdam University's Department of Slavonic Languages and Literature, but their subject changes, first from Yugoslav literature to 'Yugonostalgia', and ultimately to confrontation with the disintegration of their homeland.

Dubravka Ugresic is the author of several novels, short story collections, and books of essays, including *The Museum of Unconditional Surrender* and *Thank You For Not Reading*. Her books have been translated into more than twenty languages and she has received several major international literary awards. *The Ministry of Pain* was shortlisted for the 2006 Independent Foreign Fiction Prize.

Michael Henry Heim is Professor of Slavic Languages and Literatures at UCLA. He is well known for his translations of Milan Kundera, Danilo Kiš and Thomas Mann. He is also the Founder of the Association for the Translation of Central European Literatures, USA.

The big and little markets

A hundred metres away from the church Nyamata's main street emerges, lined with majestic umuniyinya, called 'chit-chat trees'. A wooden sign for an AIDS awareness campaign is the town's only bit of advertising. It marks the entrance to the market square, where boys, except during the scorching siesta hour, swirl around a football made from banana leaves.

Nyamata lives to the rhythm of two markets, the big and the little one. The big one takes place on Wednesdays and Saturdays, where at dawn, tradespeople lay their goods out on pieces of fabric spread on the ground. As is the case throughout Africa, the market is sectioned off in corporations. Here in one corner, fishermen's wives gather next to their fish, dried or smoked, strung together on creepers, protected from flies by the dust. In another corner are women farmers with mounds of sweet potatoes, bunches of bananas, sacks of red beans. Further on, shoes are piled up, in pairs or single, new or second hand. Stalls display luxurious cloths from Taiwan or the Congo snuggling next to piles of tee-shirts and underwear.

At the break of day, the crowd leaves little room for manoeuvre for the porters pushing long wooden barrows or for the women bearing wicker platters who keep the stalls stocked. Music is bought a little out of the way, in the street. The stall consists of a radio cassette player set on a stool for a trial listen, and three tables stocked with local music, traditional folk tunes from the Great Lakes, the melancholic songs of Annonciata Kamaliza, a famous Rwandan artist, and danceable hits from South Africa and the Congo. The music from the rest of the world is Céline Dion and Julio Iglesias.

The market is rather cheerful, modest, quite poor in fact, without jewellery stalls, without bric-a-brac traders, without anyone selling sculptures or paintings, without much in the way of bargaining or chit chat, without any flare-ups either.

As for the small market, it takes place every day on the bumpy waste ground behind the square. It's mainly a food market. Manioc is heaped up around the milling shed. The goat market is close by the slaughterhouse, in front of which stands a butcher's stall. Not far off are a veterinary pharmacy and clinic, and the cabaret – a bar – for local vets. Firewood sellers work hand in hand with charcoal merchants. You can also find cobblers remoulding flip flops, jerry cans of banana wine, jugs of buttermilk, turf and dried dung, heaps of trussed chickens, pyramids of sugar and salt, and everywhere, sacks of beans.

The market square is surrounded by shops painted in green, orange and blue, faded in the heat and dust. Half of them are shut and have been falling into ruins since the war. The other half house hairdressing salons and dark cabarets where men sip banana wine.

In Nyamata, there are no more newspaper stands or lay bookshops. For photocopies, you go to the parish bookshop. Near displays of coloured fabrics beneath shop awnings, close by the photo boutiques, seamstresses lean over wonderful black and gold Singer or Butterfly sewing machines. They stitch up torn trousers, make shirts to measure, sew hems on cloths, while their clients pay a visit to the church, to the chemist or to the local council.

Two days a week, Jeanette Ayinkamiye comes down from the hill of Kanazi to do some sewing at the market, in the midst of twenty sewing machines which clatter in the studious silence, interrupted occasionally by a burst of laughter, a snatch of advice. On these days, Jeanette wears her long Sunday dress with puffed out sleeves, but no jewellery, nor tresses, nor a fringe, all forbidden by her Pentecostal pastor.

The other days of the week, she works her family's plot. She dropped her studies after the genocide. She lives in an impeccably well-kept brick house with her two little sisters and two orphan children who she looks after, feeds, clothes and sends to school. She has never spoken to a foreigner before, but at the first meeting she agrees without hesitation to talk about herself. As the subject of her mother's death painfully and repeatedly comes up, she shows a remarkable determination to carry on.

Jeanette Ayinkamiye
17 years old, farmer and seamstress
Kinyinya (Maranyundo) hill

I was born among seven brothers and two sisters.

Papa was hacked the first day but we never found out where. All my brothers were killed shortly afterwards. With Maman and my little sisters we managed to escape into the marshes. For a month we endured beneath papyrus branches, hardly seeing nor hearing anything of the world any more.

During the day, we lay in the mud in the company of snakes and mosquitoes, to protect ourselves from interahamwe[†] attacks. At night,

---

† The extremist Hutu militia, trained by the Rwandan army and, in places, by French soldiers.

we roamed among abandoned houses looking for things to eat. Since we fed ourselves only on what we could find, we encountered many a case of diarrhoea; but fortunately it seemed that ordinary diseases, malaria and rain fever, wished to spare us this time round. We knew nothing of life any more, except that all Tutsis were being massacred where they lived and we would shortly all have to die.

It was a habit with us to hide in small groups. One day, the interahamwe sprang Maman from beneath the papyrus. She stood up, and offered them money if they would but kill her with a single machete blow. They undressed her so as to take the money fastened to her cloth. They first chopped her two arms, and next her two legs. Maman murmured, 'Saint Cécile, Saint Cécile', but she did not beg for mercy.

This thought makes me sad. But it makes me equally sad whether I recollect it by speaking aloud or silently to myself. This is why it does not embarrass me to tell you of it.

My two little sisters saw everything because they lay beside her, and they were struck too. Vanessa was wounded in the ankles. Marie-Claire in the head. The killers did not completely chop them up. Perhaps because they were in a hurry, perhaps they did so deliberately, as they had with Maman. As for me, all I could hear were noises and screams, because I was hiding in a hole a little further away. Once the interahamwe had gone, I got out and gave Maman some water to taste.

The first evening, she could still speak. She said to me, 'Jeanette, I leave without hope because I think you will soon be following me.' She was suffering very much because of the cuts, but she kept repeating to us that we were all going to die and that this filled her with even more grief. I was not bold enough to spend the night with her. I first had to look after my little sisters, who were very hurt but not dying. The following day, it was not possible to stay with her, because we were forced to hide. This was the rule of the marshes: when someone had been badly chopped, you had to abandon them there for the lack of safety.

Maman lay in agony for three days before finally dying. On the second day, she could only whisper, 'Goodbye, my children,' and ask for water, but she still could not manage to go. I could not stay long with her because of the interahamwe attacks. I could see that it was all over for her. I understood also that for certain people, abandoned by all, for whom suffering had become their last companion, death must surely have been an all too long and pointless labour. On the third day, she could not swallow any more, only moan softly and look about her. She never closed her eyes again. Her name was Agnès Nyirabuguzi. In Kinyarwandan 'Nyirabuguzi' means 'she who is fertile'. Today, I often dream of her, a very precise scene in the middle of the marsh: I look at Maman's face, I listen to her words, I give her something to drink but the water does not flow down into her throat but spills straight from her lips; and then the attackers begin their pursuit again; I get up, I start running; when I return to the swamp, I ask people for news of my Maman, but no one knows her as my Maman any more; then I wake up.

—

From *Into the Quick of Life: The Rwandan Genocide – The Survivors Speak* by **Jean Hatzfeld**, translated from the French by Gerry Feehily (Serpent's Tail 2005)

In Rwanda in 1994, 800,000 Tutsis were hacked to death with machetes by their Hutu neighbours. This count represents five-sixths of the Tutsi population. In the villages of Nyamata and N'tarama, where more than 10,000 Tutsis were massacred in the first two days, Jean Hatzfeld interviewed some of the survivors. Their stories of horror contrast profoundly with his own subtle and vivid descriptions of Rwanda's countryside after the genocide.

Born in Madagascar, **Jean Hatzfeld** worked for several years as a foreign correspondent for the French newspaper *Libération*, covering the conflict in Yugoslavia, where he was shot and wounded in 1992, and the Rwandan genocide. *Into the Quick of Life* won the 2000 Prix France Culture.

Gerry Feehily lived in Ireland, Italy, Spain, Germany and Japan before settling in Paris in the mid-1990s. He is English site editor and resident blogger at www.presseurop.eu and *Courrier International*, and a journalist specialising in literature and European politics. His work has appeared in the *Guardian*, the *Independent*, *New Statesman*, *Irish Examiner*, *Spiked* and *3am*. He has also translated Pavel Hak's novel *Sniper*, and his novel *Fever* was published in 2007.

Gate of the sun

Hey, you!

How am I supposed to talk to you, or with you or about you?

Should I tell you stories you already know, or be silent and let you go wherever it is you go? I come close to you, walking on tiptoe so as not to wake you, and then I laugh at myself because all I want is to wake you. I need one thing – one thing, dear God: that this man, drowning in his own eyes, should get up, should open his eyes and say something.

But I'm lying.

Did you know you've turned me into a liar?

I say I want one thing, but I want thousands of things. I lie, God take pity on you, on me and on your poor mother. Yes, we forgot your mother. You told me all your stories, and you never told me how your mother died. You told about the death of your blind father and how you slipped into Galilee and attended his funeral. You stood on the hill above the village of Deir El Asad, seeing but unseen, weeping and not weeping.

At the time I believed you. I believed that intuition had led you to your house there, hours before he died.

But now I don't.

At the time I was bewitched by your story. Now the spell is broken, and I no longer believe.

But your mother?

Why didn't you say anything about her death?

Is your mother dead?

Do you remember the story of the icon of the Virgin Mary?

We were living through the civil war in Lebanon, and you were saying that war shouldn't be like that. You even advised me, when I came back from Beijing as a doctor, not to take part in the war, and asked me to go with you to Palestine.

'But you don't go to fight, Yunis my friend. You go because of your wife.'

You gave me a long lecture about the meaning of war and then said something about the picture of the Virgin Mary in your house, and that was when I asked you if your mother was Christian and how the sheikh of the village of Ein El Zeitoun could have married a Christian woman. You explained that she wasn't a Christian but loved the Virgin and used to put her picture under her pillow, and that she'd made you love the Virgin too because she was the mistress of all the world's women and because her picture was beautiful – a woman bending her head over her son, born swaddled in his shroud.

'And what did the sheikh think?'I asked you.

It was then that you explained to me that your father the sheikh was blind, and that he never saw the picture at all.

When did Naheeleh tell you of your mother's death?

Why don't you tell me? Is it because your wife said your mother had asked to be buried with the picture and this caused a problem in the village?

Why do you sleep like that and not answer?

You sleep like sleep itself. You sleep in sleep, and drown. The doctor said you had a blood clot on the brain, were clinically dead, and there was no hope. I ordered him to get out of my way and refused to believe him.

I see you in front of me and can do nothing.

I hold conversations with you, and I tell you stories. I'll tell you everything. What do you say – I'll make tea, and we'll sit on the low chairs in front of your house and tell tales! You used to laugh at me because I don't smoke. You used to smoke your cigarette right to the end, chewing on the butt hanging between your lips and sucking in the smoke.

Now here I am. I close the door of your room. I sit next to you. I light a cigarette, draw the smoke deep into my lungs, and I tell you tales. And you don't answer.

Why don't you talk to me?

The tea's gone cold, and I'm tired. You're immersed in the process of breathing and don't care.

Please don't believe them.

Do you remember the day when you came to me and said that everyone was sick of you, and I couldn't dispel the sadness from your round white face? What was I supposed to say? Should I have said your day had passed, or hadn't yet come? You'd have been even more upset, and I couldn't lie to you. So I'm sad too, and my sadness is a deep breach in my soul that I can't repair, but I swear I don't want you to die.

Why did you lie to me?

Why did you tell me after the mourners had left that Naheeleh's death didn't matter, because a woman only dies if her man stops loving her, and Naheeleh hadn't died, because you still loved her?

'She's here,' you said, and you pointed at your eyes, wide open to show their dark grey. I was never able to identify the colour of your eyes – when I asked you, you would say that Naheeleh didn't know what colour they were either, and that at Bab El Shams she used to ask you about the colours of things. You lied to me.

You convinced me that Naheeleh hadn't died, and didn't finish the sentence. At the time I didn't take in what you'd said; I thought they were the beautiful words an old lover uses to heal his love – but death was in the other half of the sentence, because a man dies when his woman stops loving him, and you're dying because Naheeleh stopped loving you when she died.

So here you are, drowsing.

Dear God, what drowsiness is this? And why do I feel a deathly drowsiness when I'm near you? I lean back in the chair and sleep. When I get up in the middle of the night, I feel pain all over my body.

I come close to you, I see the air roiling around you, and I see that place I haven't visited. I'd decided to go; everyone goes, so why not me? I'd go and have a look. I'd go and anchor the landmarks in my eyes. You used to tell me that you knew the sites because they were engraved on your eyes like indelible landmarks.

Where are the landmarks, my friend? How shall I know the road, and who will guide me?

You told me about the caves dug out of the rocks. Is it true that you used to meet her there? Or were you lying to me? You said they were called Bab El Shams – Gate of the Sun – and smiled and said you didn't mean the Shams I was in love with, or that terrible massacre at El Miyyeh wi-Miyyeh camp, where they killed her.

You told me I didn't love Shams and should forget her: 'If you loved her, you'd avenge her. It can't be love, son. You love a woman who doesn't love you, and that's an impossibility.'

You don't understand. How can I avenge a woman who was killed because of another man?

'So she didn't love you,' you said.

'She did but in her own way,' I answered.

'Love has a thousand doors. But one-sided love isn't a door, it's a delusion.'

I didn't tell you then that your love for Naheeleh may have been a delusion too, because you only met her on journeys that resembled dreams.

I draw close to tell you that the moon is full. In El Ghabsiyyeh, we love the moon, and we fear it. When it's full, we don't sleep.

Get up and look at the moon.

You didn't tell me about your mother, but I'm going to tell you about mine. The truth is, I don't know much about her – she disappeared. They said she'd gone to her people in Amman, and when I was in Jordan in 1970 I looked for her, but that's another tale I'll tell you later.

I told you about my mother, and I'm going to tell you again. When you were telling me about Bab El Shams, you used to say that stories are like wine: they mature in the telling. Does that mean that the telling of a story is like the jar it's kept in? You used to tell the stories of Naheeleh over and over again, your eyes shining with the same desire.

'She cast a spell on me, that woman,' you'd say.

But I know that the spellbinder was you – how else did you persuade Naheeleh to put up with you, reeking with the stink of travel?

My mother used to wake me while it was still night in the camp and whisper to me, and I'd get up and see the moon in its fullness, and not go back to sleep.

The woman from El Kweikat said we were mad: 'Ghabsiyyeh people are crazy, because they're afraid of the moon.' But we weren't afraid – though in fact, yes, we did stay awake all night. My mother wouldn't let me sleep. She'd tie a black scarf around her head and ask me to look at the face of the moon so I could see my dead father's face.

'Do you see him?' she'd ask.

I'd say that I saw him, though I swear I didn't. But now, can you believe it, now, after years and years, when I look at the face of the moon, I see my father's face, stained with blood. My mother said they killed him, left him in a heap at the door and went off. She said he fell in a heap as though he wasn't a man but a sack, and when she went over to him, she didn't see him. They took him and buried him in secret in the Martyrs' Cemetery. 'Look at your father and tell him what you want.'

I used to look and not see, but I wouldn't say. Now I see, but what am I supposed to say?

Get up, man, and look at the face of the moon. Do you see your wife? Do you see my father? Certainly you will never see my mother, and even if you see her, you will never know her. Even I have forgotten her, forgotten her voice and her tears. The only thing I remember is the taste of the dough she used to make in the clay oven in front of our house. She would put red pepper, oil, cumin and onions on a piece of dough and bake it. Then she'd make tea and eat, and I'd eat with her, and we'd look at the moon. That burning taste overwhelms my tongue and my eyes, and I drink tea and look at the moon, and I see.

My mother told me that in my father's village they didn't sleep. When the moon grew round and sat on the dish of the sky, the whole village would wake up, and the blind singer would sit in the square and play his one-stringed fiddle, singing to the night as though he was weeping. And I am weeping with drowsiness, and the taste of the hot pepper, and what seem to be dreams.

The moon is full, my swimmer in white sheets. Get up and look and drink tea with me. Or didn't you people in Ein El Zeitoun get up when the moon was full?

But you're not from Ein El Zeitoun. Well, you are from Ein El Zeitoun, but your blind father moved to Deir El Asad after the village was massacred in 1948.

You were born in Ein El Zeitoun, and they called you Yunis. You told me your blind father named you Yunis – Jonah – because, like Jonah, you'd vanquished death.

You didn't tell me about your mother; it was Amna who told me. She claimed to be your cousin on your father's side and had come to help you put the house to rights. She was also beautiful. Why did you get angry with me that day? I swear I didn't mean anything by it. I smiled – and you glowered, went out of the house and left me with her.

You came into your house, and you saw me sitting with Amna, who was giving me some water. She told me she knew everything about me because you'd told her, and she asked me to watch out for you because she couldn't always come from Ein El Hilweh camp to Shatila. I smiled at you and winked, and from that day on I never saw Amna at your house again. I swear I didn't mean anything. Well, I did mean something, but when all's said and done you're a man, so you shouldn't get angry. People are like that, they've been that way since Adam, God grant him peace, and people betray the ones they love; they betray them and they regret it; they betray them because they love them, so what's the problem?

It's a terrible thing. Why did you tell Amna to stop visiting you? Was it because she loved you? I know – when I see a woman in love, I know. She overflows with love and becomes soft and undulating. Not men. Men are to be pitied because they don't know that softness that floods and leavens the muscles.

Amna loved you, but you refused to marry her. She told me about it, just as she told me other things she made me swear I'd never mention in front of you. I'm released from my oath now because you can't hear, and even if you could there'd be nothing you could do. All you could say is that Amna was a liar and end the conversation.

From *Gate of the Sun* by **Elias Khoury**, translated from the Arabic by
Humphrey Davies (Harvill Secker 2005)

In a makeshift hospital in a refugee camp on the outskirts of Beirut, Yunis,
an ageing Palestinian freedom fighter, lies in a coma. In an attempt to
revive his patient, Khaleel, his spiritual son, like a modern-day Sheherazade
begins telling Yunis the stories of their people's exile in Lebanon.

Elias Khoury was born in Lebanon, and was the editor-in-chief of the
cultural supplement of Beirut's daily newspaper, *An-Nahar*. He is now a
Global Distinguished Professor of Middle Eastern and Islamic Studies at
New York University. He is regarded as one of the finest Arabic writers of
his generation, and in 2000 was awarded the Prize of Palestine for *Gate
of the Sun*.

Humphrey Davies is an award-winning translator from Arabic. He has
translated works by Naguib Mahfouz, Alaa Al-Aswany, Ahmed Alaidy,
Gamal Al-Ghitani and Ahlam Mosteghanemi. He also translated the Arab
Booker Award-winning novel *Sunset Oasis* by Bahaa Taher.

Virtually unveiled women

Blogs have allowed some Iranian women to express themselves freely for the first time in modern history and this small freedom may have a big knock-on effect. It might be objected that the majority of female bloggers do not reflect a true cross-section of Iranian society, as not everyone has access to computers and the Internet. However, thanks to the Islamic Republic's policy of free education and its national literacy campaigns, those who enter further education tend to be from a relatively wide cross-section of society. Iranian students come from a broad variety of social and regional backgrounds and have access to the Internet.

Veil or be damned

On 7 March 1979 Ayatollah Khomeini decreed that women were required to wear the veil. Ironically, the ruling came a day before the scheduled celebrations throughout Iran to mark International Women's Day. The gatherings soon turned into mass protests against Khomeini's decree and his annulment of the Family Rights Act [by which women lost many rights at a stroke and were in future deemed legally to be worth half the value of

Above: Women demonstrating against newly introduced laws of compulsory Hejab
Right: Shahran mountains, Tehran, Iran (2001).

men]. This was also the first reported outing of a group calling themselves Hezbollah or the 'Party of God', who fiercely attacked many of the demonstrators.

18 January 2004

Some of you may remember the beginning of the Revolution, but for those who aren't old enough: until 1979 women did not have to wear the veil ... but soon there were cries of 'Veil or be eaten!'... And in next to no time an evil institution for the enforcement of rules called the Revolutionary Komiteh raised its head. So in 1979 women put on headscarves, but they were still free to go out with a shirt and skirt or a dress...

Do you remember the first manteaus? Big shapeless, floor-length coats that women wore on top of their ordinary clothes ... As times passed different versions of the manteau came out... I remember during those early years suddenly manteaus made in a 'jean' fabric became fashionable, but before long the 'brothers' from the Komiteh would roam the streets and bazaars with carpet cutters, slashing through these manteaus (at the same time tearing through the flesh of the poor unfortunate characters that had taken up this trend). Well, the jean fabric was a representation of the 'great Satan', America...

Soon fitted manteaus became fashionable. Fitted around the waist, with the shape of the women's breasts visible... these naturally put into question and demeaned the value of women... anyway in next to no time they went out of fashion. And then it was the turn of the Maxi manteaus with slits! But oh! these slits were just too much for the 'brothers' of the Komiteh, who were aroused at the spectacle... So people gave in by sewing buttons on the slits ... Then capes were the latest thing... except now voices were raised that they were too short and a vision of depravity... but once women had got them this short they soon evolved into the tight and short manteaus...

The point is, that as long as you wear a manteau you will not be 'endangering Islam'. Like this woman in the photo, paragliding in Tehran, she is still wearing her manteau with her special gear.

By Shima

Under the veil

According to historical accounts the veil predates Islam by many centuries. Assyrian kings first introduced it in the Near East, along with the seclusion of women in the royal harem. It was only in the second Islamic century that the veil became common. It was first used among the powerful and rich as a status symbol – then only 'common' women would be seen in the streets unveiled. Later the Koranic instruction to 'tell the believing women to lower their gaze and protect their private parts and not to show off their adornment except only that which is apparent and to draw their veils all over their bosoms' was taken by some as a ruling to veil one's hair, neck and ears.

For a woman to assume a shielding veil and stay within the house was a sign of status: it showed that her family had the means to enable her to do so.

Throughout Islamic history only certain sections of the urban classes were veiled and secluded. Rural and nomadic women – the majority of the population – were not. Even after the 1979 ruling banning women from appearing unveiled, Iran's ancient indigenous tribal women rarely adhered to the revolutionary rules for women and could at times even be observed riding their horses into town, when urban women could be flogged or imprisoned for riding bicycles.

Many of Iran's tribal women refuse to comply with the Islamic Republic's dress codes – much more so than urban women, who are strictly policed. Take the woman from Iran's ancient Ghasgai tribe in the above photograph: her hair is showing through the decorated gauze fabric that Ghasgai women often wear. The Basij responsible for keeping the morality laws in place

Bottom left A tribal woman in Iran (2003). Bottom middle: A woman from the Ghasgai Tribe (2003) Bottom right: A tribal woman in Northern Iran.

would never dare approach such women, for fear of offending the strict 'Islamic honour codes' of the indigenous tribes and starting widespread tribal rebellions against the regime.

8 March 2004

Why is it that women in villages are so much freer in comparison with our urban women (at least when it comes to choosing what to wear)? It's incredible but they are not only freer in how they dress, but also in their activities and movements. Why is it that they don't 'endanger Islam' by not wearing headscarves, as they freely mingle, laughing and chatting with the menfolk? Is it due to their heavy participation in work? Or is it that work will be stopped without women? God Forbid!

16 January 2003

Has anyone ever explained why it is that in our Persian language we do not have masculine or feminine verbs or even 'he' or 'she', as they do in English? We say 'Oou', meaning either 'her' or 'him'… Even though Persian is sophisticated and complex, we do not differentiate men and women in our speech…

I am taking an English course right now and our professor has said that there are many Farsi words that basically do not have English equivalents... Especially words related to feelings and emotions (yup! evidence that we are all a bunch of lovesick fools)…

Why is it then that our ancestors did not feel the necessity to distinguish between the sexes when it came to our language? So where did we inherit this chauvinistic present-day culture from?

By borderline

10 December 2002

Women in Iran have been forced to embody the value systems of society through their dress and social behaviour. Yet today many young Iranian women reject such an imposition and, in turn, have consistently flouted the rules through their dress and behaviour. This tendency is marked in the blogs of young Iranian women and some routinely mock the whole idea of a 'revolutionary hejab'.

From My Personal Street Research. If you wear a short jacket, lots of make-up and a shawl hanging loosely over your head, all men in Tehran will come on to you.

If you wear a tight short jean manteau, lots of make-up, have strands of hair strategically showing, 80 per cent of men in Tehran will come on to you.

If you wear a tight black manteau above the knee, use your dark glasses as an Alice-band, with a thin black scarf, 70 per cent of men in Tehran will come on to you.

If you wear a baggy cream long robe, lots of make-up, and have a few strands of hair showing, 60 per cent of men in Tehran will come on to you.

If you wear long black robes, no make-up, and no hair showing, 30 per cent of men in Tehran will come on to you...

A chador and no make-up... will not get you a man.

From **We Are Iran**, edited and translated from the Farsi by Nasrin Alavi (Portobello Books 2005)

We Are Iran is a multi-voiced bloggers' portrait of contemporary Iran. In cyberspace Iranians rapidly found a freedom to express opinions that was not available to them in print. The Iran described in their blogs is not the dour nation of ayatollahs and militias, but a country where 70 per cent of the population is under 30 and finds the Islamist fundamentalists antiquated. Their voices – infused with Persian lyricism – are refreshing and utterly at odds with the vision of the country that normally prevails in the West.

Nasrin Alavi spent her formative years in Iran. After attending university in the UK and working in the city of London and academia she returned to her birthplace working for an NGO for a number of years. Today she lives in the UK. This is her first book.

The last autumn of the nomadic aul

At the end of 1930, and in the winter of 1931, the Kazakh people's age-old nomadic way of life finally came to an end. The clans were all joined together into collective farms, and each aul settled in one place for good. Many years have gone by since then, and we who experienced the joys and freedom of the wandering way of life tend to remember none of the hardships involved, but only the good things: the green carpet of meadows stretching out before us as we arrived at our summer stopping place, the unforgettable scent of the wild flowers and the blaze of colour they created all around, and the cool, fresh breeze blowing from the snowy peaks.

In autumn, when most of the men were busy with harvesting and haymaking, it was rare for people to come visiting, but once in a while groups of elders would do so for old times' sake, and sit around drinking mare's milk and discussing the issues of the day. Mare's milk was kept chiefly as a drink for guests, and it was very popular: at less busy times men would ride round the aul in groups every morning until midday, visiting the yurts with foals tethered outside to quench their thirst. Fermented in a specially made leather flask called a saba, the milk contains much less fat than that of cows and goats, and if well prepared has a sourish-sweet taste.

In 1930, the main topic of conversation was the daily news brought to the steppe by word of mouth (the so-called *uzyn kulak* – 'long ear' – of the steppe telegraph), which was our only source of information. Because we did not have radios or telephones, or even a postal service, it could take up to a year for information about new laws or important events to reach the far-flung regions of the country. The grandiose propaganda campaigns aimed at the masses had yet to get underway, and any news was passed on from one person to the next in the form of stories with a great many embroidered details. But in any case, ordinary people were more interested in local matters, and simply did not have the time or inclination to pay attention to things on a grander scale: all the elders wanted to find out about the new laws and orders issued by the aul council, since this was, as far as they were concerned, the highest authority in the land.

'What we used to call a 'region' is now going to be called a 'district''. Someone in the know would start the conversation along these lines, having just discovered what had been enacted two years previously.

'An official came to the aul council from this district centre and gathered together our activists and told them that all the people and their livestock and property, wives and servants, children and grandchildren were going to be collectivised and everything would belong to everyone,' another would announce to the alarm of everyone present.

'I've heard that all the people are going to be housed under one roof,' a third would say, 'and everyone's going to go to bed at the same time, and eat and drink together and get up at the same time. Everyone's going to be taken to work in a formation and then brought back in one.' And seeing that he had shocked his companions even more, he would beam with delight.

'It's not like that at all – I heard it with my own ears. They're only going to take away the horses and other working animals to use as transport, and people are going to get together and plough the land and sow wheat all together so that there is more wheat in the country. Maybe, who knows, there's some truth to it somewhere? When a lot of people get together to help someone hard up and work together at haymaking, say, or when a new crop is being harvested, everyone tries to work faster than the person next to them, and the work goes like a dream! You know, you've all done it yourselves. If you've got all sorts of machinery, and horses and oxen, and you get everyone to work together, the results are sure to be very good indeed.'

'I don't know about that: when a lot of people get together to do a job, the result is usually not much good. And when we went and helped out those people who were hard up, there were some slackers who didn't even bother to turn up.'

Yet another of the elders would interrupt, 'This society uniting all peasants has already got a name: it's going to be called a 'commune'. Before he died, Lenin instructed his aides to get all the peasants to join together. But the people who took over running the country from him forgot all about his instructions. Lenin's widow who, they say, is still alive, went to see Stalin – that's his name, apparently – who was left in charge and said to him: 'Why have you comrades-in-arms of Lenin forgotten all about his instructions? Why aren't you joining the peasants together in collective farms and communes? If you don't obey the Leader's orders, you'll anger his spirit!'

After hearing this story, one of the others would offer a logical conclusion of his own – 'As always, a woman's to blame for the trouble' – before someone else had the last word:

'Everything that's been said here is complete rubbish. And the bit about the collective farms and communes – they've all been thought up by the aul activists. What good is Lenin's wife to us lot here when all the power is in their hands? The power's completely gone to their heads and made them barking mad because they have no idea what to do with it. People who have never managed to run their own affairs are now in charge of people's lives. How can a society be run by people who never obeyed their grandfathers or listened to their wisdom? It reminds me of the old saying, 'When there's no lord, a slave will take his place, and when there's no dog, a pig will guard the yard!"

Such was our community's grasp of the innovations which were to change our lives in ways we could not even remotely imagine.

I still did not understand much about the events taking place in my aul, but I must have heard thousands of lengthy conversations like this one on all sorts of topics. We were always receiving visits from other people, whether neighbours or relatives and guests from other regions. This was partly because all our kinsmen made their mare's milk in our yurt, and partly because people came to pay their respects to my 85-year-old grandmother, who was held in very high regard.

Since we were frequently on the move, our neighbours kept changing as well. The summer pastures and winter stopping places were often far apart, so summer neighbours did not see each other all winter. To make up for it, kinsmen would meet up in their regular spring stopping place, and distant relatives and people from other clans would congregate in camps in the summer months. People would pay each other visits, exchange gifts and eat together – the entire aul would put on a big feast for another aul. In addition, the custom was that any aul recently settled in a new place had to help and support the next aul to arrive by preparing a hot meal and carrying it over to them, since they would be too busy unpacking to cook for themselves.

Our winter stopping place as situated in the territory of a branch of the Karagerei clan named after the 'six fair-haired Naiman', and outside the lands of our Otei clan. My grandmother Aksha was an Aknaiman by birth, from the eminent Konakbayev clan, so as soon as our aul arrived nearly all the most senior members of the Aknaiman family would visit our home to welcome her and wish us happiness and prosperity and rich grazing for our livestock. The village and regional centre of Kumashkino, now renamed Kurchum, was about twenty kilometres away, and members of the Aknaiman family would always stay with us on their way to and from the large market and fair held there every Sunday. And in the spring when our aul was going back to its clan's territory, there would be a similar influx of people wishing to say goodbye. This would continue for nearly a month, until the end of the breeding season.

Similarly, when summer came and we moved up into the hills, relatives and friends who had not seen each other for a whole year would start meeting up again. Communities of different families would live side-by-side during the summer months: the Bur clan would come from the south, descendants of the Zharke and Andagul clans from the west, and the Saryzhomart clan from the east – and they all made special visits to pay their respects to my grandmother. The most important visitors were treated not only to mare's milk, but to special portions of our winter stocks of meat which had been put by.

I remember two guests in particular. One was Mamyr Altybayev, who had governed the Kumashinko region in pre-Soviet days; the other was called Yestaulet Yesberdinov. They were descended from two of our great-grandfather Otei's sons, and Mamyr was the same age as Toimbai-ata, while Yestaulet belonged to my grandfather's generation.

Mamyr was a taciturn, stocky man with a grey-flecked, black beard and swarthy complexion. In his rare visits to different aul he was always accompanied by an entourage, just as he had been in the old days. His countrymen continued to respect him and pay him homage, though as a governor in tsarist times he had apparently kept the province on a tight rein, occasionally losing his temper and cracking his whip, and had not been averse to receiving 'gifts'. He was said to be particularly strict when it came to collecting taxes, and once, when the members of Administrative Aul Number Seven were late paying, he had begun confiscating livestock and extracting fines despite pleas for clemency from some extremely impoverished families. The local aul poet Meirembai Baspakov had written a poem in response, saying that the governor had amassed quite enough for himself by taking extra taxes from the Taz and Zharylgap clans, and extracting more from a small number of very poor members of the Bur clan would not make him any richer.

Subsequently, in 1926, as a rich landowner, Mamyr Altybayev had all his stock confiscated and was deported to the town of Rubtsovsk, 200 miles north of Ust-Kamenogorsk. After escaping a year later, he secretly gathered together a great many relatives, including his children and grandchildren, and emigrated with them to China. According to people who saw him there, he led a modest life as a poor stock-breeder. One day, on the way to a neighbouring aul on his only horse, which was harnessed to a cart carrying his two daughters-in-law, he accidentally drove over the edge of a local landowner's crop while turning a fork in the road and got badly beaten up. The women burst into floods of tears and wailed, 'How could that filthy Chinaman dare lay a finger on you and injure your noble body?' To which, apparently, Mamyr replied, 'Never mind! It's made me think about the times I used a whip on the backs of my own countrymen.'

My family, and especially we children, always looked forward to seeing the other person we all held in great esteem, Yestaulet Yesberdinov. Every time he visited our yurt, he would bring grandmother a gift of a large lump of sugar shaped like a horse's head. As we hardly ever had sugar or, for that matter, any sweet foods, this was a great treat for us. Tall and lean, Grandfather Yestaulet had a long beard and always wore silver-framed glasses. He used to visit us as soon as our aul settled in the mountain meadows for the summer. As he stepped through the doorway, he would greet my grandmother, whom he had known since childhood, with the words, 'Hello, my ancient friend! Are you fit and well?'

Then they would greet each other in a traditional manner which is hardly remembered any more. My grandmother would silently advance towards her guest with her arms outstretched to the side and palms forward. As they drew near each other somewhere in the middle of the yurt, they would keep their arms outstretched like wings and press the palms of their hands together. Then, their chests touching, they would half-turn their bodies to the right and left before slowly bringing their arms together until they were outstretched between them. They would gently stroke each other's arms with their palms, and finally both touch their own faces with their palms. This was known as a 'greeting in embraces'.

A Kazakh greeting took a long time but few words were exchanged in the process. The greeting consisted of conventional questions and replies from all present. It began with the traditional 'Assalai magaleikum!' and the reply 'Aleikum assalaam!', which mean, 'Peace to your house!' and 'Peace to your house also!' These were followed by enquiries after the health of mostly the eldest in the household: were the person's body and stomach healthy, were the person's arms and legs functioning well, were the people and animals, children, grandchildren and other family members and relatives in good health? Were the corrals and pens for the livestock in good order? Were all the aul in the area fit and well? Were they having trouble with any animals or birds of prey? The host would reply succinctly to these questions: 'Thank God, everything is in order' and then ask about his guest's affairs after each subsequent question. Congratulations would be offered in respect of any joyful celebration that had taken place since they last met, such as the birth of a child, a wedding, or a son's or daughter's engagement party. If a son was getting married, the guest would say he hoped the son's bride entered the household 'light-footed' (happily, in other words), and if a daughter was getting married, he would wish her happiness in her new home and family.

Yestaulet and my grandmother would sometimes spend a whole day sitting next to each other and talking. The rest of the family tried not to interrupt them, and I still recall how emotionally Yestaulet said goodbye at the end of their last meeting. Taking my grandmother's hands and squeezing them tightly, he said, 'Dear Aksha, keep alive and well. I wonder if we'll ever see each other again and have another chance to talk?' Then he held onto her hands for a while.

'That is up to God!' she replied. But he answered slowly and tearfully, 'It's unlikely…'

At the age of 85, he had good grounds for this belief. Six months later, realising he might soon be prosecuted, imprisoned and stripped of his property, he set out with his family to escape to China. But his heart could not bear the pain of leaving his homeland, and he died on the journey to the border.

—

From *The Silent Steppe* by **Mukhamet Shayakhmetov**, translated from the Russian by Jan Butler and edited by Anthony Gardner (Stacey International 2006)

The Silent Steppe is the story of Mukhamet Shayakhmetov, born into a family of nomadic Kazakh herdsmen in 1922, the year of the consolidation of Soviet rule across his people's vast steppe-land in central Asia. Ten years later, collectivisation of agriculture was forcibly imposed, and well over a million Kazakhs died, more than a quarter of the indigenous population across a territory as great as western Europe. Of this, the outside world knew nothing.

Mukhamet Shayakhmetov is a Kazakh born and bred. He retired in 1981 as a headmaster and head of the local education department. He and his wife Nurkamal have a growing number of descendants, all offspring of the original Kazakh nomads.

Jan Butler's translations from the Russian include major works of fiction by some of Russia's most eminent writers, together with biographies, screenplays and operatic librettos.

Allah is not obliged

The full, final and completely complete title of my bullshit story is: *Allah is not obliged to be fair about all the things he does here on earth*. Okay. Right. I better start explaining some stuff.

First off, Number one... My name is Birahima and I'm a little nigger. Not 'cos I'm black and I'm a kid. I'm a little nigger because I can't talk French for shit. That's how things are. You might be a grown-up, or old, you might be Arab, or Chinese, or white, or Russian – or even American – if you talk bad French, it's called *parler petit nègre* – little nigger talking – so that makes you a little nigger too. That's the rules of French for you.

Number two... I didn't get very far at school; I gave up in my third year in primary school. I chucked it because everyone says education's not worth an old grandmother's fart any more. (In Black Nigger African Native talk, when a thing isn't worth much we say it's not worth an old grandmother's fart, on account of how a fart from a fucked-up old granny doesn't hardly make any noise and it doesn't even smell really bad.) Education isn't worth a grandmother's fart any more, because nowadays even if you get a degree you've got no hope of becoming a nurse or a teacher in some fucked-up French-speaking banana republic. ('Banana republic' means it looks democratic, but really it's all corruption and vested interests.) But going to primary school for three years doesn't make you all autonomous and incredible. You know a bit, but not enough; you end up being what Black Nigger African Natives call grilled on both sides. You're not an indigenous savage any more like the rest of the Black Nigger African Natives 'cos you can understand the civilised blacks and the *toubabs* (a *toubab* is a white person) and work out what they're saying, except maybe English people and the American Blacks in Liberia, but you still don't know how to do geography or grammar or conjugation or long division or comprehension so you'll never get the easy money working as a civil servant in some fucked-up, crooked republic like Guinea, Côte d'Ivoire, etc., etc.

Number three... I'm disrespectful, I'm rude as a goat's beard and I swear like a bastard. I don't swear like the civilised Black Nigger African Natives in their nice suits, I don't say fuck! shit! bitch! I use Malinké swear words like *faforo!* (my father's cock – or your father's or somebody's father's), *gnamokodé!* (bastard), *walahé!* (I swear by Allah). Malinké is the name of the tribe I belong to. They're Black Nigger African Savages and there's a lot of us in the north of Côte d'Ivoire and in Guinea, and there's even Malinkés in other corrupt fucked-up banana republics like Gambia, Sierra Leone and up in Senegal.

Number four... I suppose I should apologise for talking right at you like this, on account of how I'm only a kid. I'm maybe ten, maybe twelve (two years ago, grandmother said I was eight, maman said I was ten) and I talk too much. Polite kids are supposed to listen, they don't sit under that talking-tree and they don't chatter like a mynah bird in a fig tree. Talking is for old men with big white beards. There's a proverb that says, 'For as long as there's a head on your shoulders, you don't put your headdress on your knee.' That's village customs for you. But I don't give two fucks about village customs any more, 'cos I've been in Liberia and killed lots of guys with an AK-47 (we called it a 'kalash') and got fucked-up on kanif and lots of hard drugs.

Number five... To make sure I tell you the life story of my fucked-up life in proper French, I've got four different dictionaries so I don't get confused with big words. First off, I've got the *Larousse* and the *Petit Robert*, then, second off, I've got the *Glossary of French Lexical Particularities in Black Africa*, and, third off, I've got the *Harrap's*. The dictionaries are for looking up big words and checking big words and particularly for explaining big words. I need to be able to explain stuff because I want all sorts of different people to read my bullshit: colonial *toubabs*, Black Nigger African Natives and anyone that can understand French. The *Larousse* and the *Petit Robert* are for looking up and checking and explaining French words so I can explain them to Black Nigger African Natives. The *Glossary of French Lexical Particularities in Black Africa* is for explaining African words to the French *toubabs* from France. The *Harrap's* is for explaining pidgin words to French people who don't know shit about pidgin.

How did I get the dictionaries? That's a long story that I don't feel like going into right now. Because I haven't got time 'cos I don't want to get tied up in bullshit. That's why. *Faforo!*

Number six... Don't go thinking that I'm some cute kid, 'cos I'm not. I'm cursed because I did bad things to my maman. According to Black Nigger African Native customs, if your mother is angry with you and she dies with all that anger in her heart, then she curses you and you're cursed. And afterwards nothing ever goes right for you or anyone who knows you.

I'm not some cute kid on account of how I'm hunted by the *gnamas* of lots of people. (*Gnamas* is a complicated Black Nigger African Native word that I need to explain so French people can understand. According to the

Glossary, a *gnama* is the shadow of a person that remains after death. The shadow becomes an immanent malevolent force which stalks anyone who has killed an innocent victim.) And I killed lots of innocent victims over in Liberia and Sierra Leone where I was a child doing tribal warfare, and where I got fucked-up on lots of hard drugs. The *gnamas* of the innocent people I killed are stalking me, so my whole life and everything round me is fucked. *Gnamokodé!*

So that's me – six points, no more no less, with my cheeky foul-mouthed attitude thrown in for good treasure. (Actually, you don't say 'for good treasure', you say 'for good measure'. I need to explain 'for good measure' for Black Nigger African Natives who don't know nothing about anything. According to *Larousse*, it means extra, on top of everything else.)

So that's me, and it's not an edifying spectacle. Anyway, now that I've introduced myself, I'm really, truly going to tell you the life story of my cursed, fucked-up life.

Sit down and listen. And write everything down. *Allah is not obliged to be fair about everything he does. Faforo!*

Before I got to Liberia, I was a fearless, blameless kid. I slept anywhere I wanted and stole all kinds of stuff to eat. My grandmother used to spend days and days looking for me: that's because I was what they call a street kid. Before I was a street kid, I went at school. Before that, I was a *bilakoro* back in the village of Togobala (according to the *Glossary*, a *bilakoro* is an uncircumcised boy). I ran through the streams and down to the fields and I hunted mice and birds in the scrubland. I was a proper Black Nigger African Native Savage. Before that, I was a baby in maman's hut. I used to scamper between maman's hut and grandmother's hut. Before that, I crawled around in maman's hut. Before I was crawling around on all fours, I was in maman's belly. And before that, I could have been the wind, or maybe a snake, or maybe water. You're always something like a snake or a tree or an animal or a person before you get born. It's called life before life. I lived life before life. *Gnamokodé!*

The first thing inside me.... In proper French, you don't say 'inside me', you say 'in my mind'. Well, the first thing inside me or in my mind when I think about maman's hut is the fire, the glow of the embers, the flicker of flame. I don't know how many months old I was when I grilled my arm. Maman hadn't been counting my age, she hadn't got time on account of how she spent all the time suffering and crying.

I forgot to tell you something major, something really extremely important. Maman walked round on her arse. *Walahé!* On the two cheeks of her arse. She propped herself up on her hands and her left leg. Her left leg was as withered as a shepherd's crook and her right leg – the one she called her crushed serpent's head – was amputated and crippled by the ulcer. (According to my *Larousse*, an 'ulcer' is 'an inflammatory and often suppurating lesion on the skin or an internal mucous surface resulting in necrosis of tissue'). It's like a blister that never gets better and ends up killing you. Maman's ulcer was swathed in leaves wrapped up in an old *pagne* (a loin-cloth). Her right leg was permanently sticking up in the air. Maman moved on her arse like a caterpillar in fits and starts ('fits and starts' means 'stopping suddenly then starting again'). I was still crawling back then. I could tell you what happened, I can remember. But I don't like to tell everyone about it. Because it's a secret, because when I tell the story I tremble from the pain like I'm terrified on account of the fire searing in my skin. I was running around on all fours and maman was chasing me. I was going faster than she was. She was chasing after me, her right leg stuck up in the air, moving on her arse in fits and starts, leaning on her arms. I went too far, too fast, 'cos I was trying not to get caught. I made a dash and fell on to the glowing embers. The fire did its job and grilled my arm. It grilled the arm of a poor little kid because Allah doesn't have to be fair about everything he does here on earth. I still have the scar, on my arm, in my head, in my belly like the Black Africans say, and in my heart. It's still there in my heart, in my whole being, like the smell of my mother. My body is saturated with maman's nauseating smell. (According to the Larousse, 'nauseating' means 'capable of arousing aversion or disgust' and 'saturated' means 'drenched or soaked with liquid'.) *Gnamokodé!*

From *Allah Is Not Obliged* by **Ahmadou Kourouma**, translated from the French by Frank Wynne (William Heinemann 2006)

Ahmadou Kourouma's penultimate novel is a story of violence and laughter. After Birahima's mother dies, he travels to Liberia to find his aunt, but on the way gets caught up in rebel fighting and ends up with a Kalashnikov in his hands. An African *Candide*, he recounts his chaotic adventures as a child soldier with poker-faced bravado and precocious wisdom.

Born in 1927 on the Ivory Coast, **Ahmadou Kourouma** fought in the French colonial army in Indochina and studied science in France. Returning to the Ivory Coast, he fell foul of the regime and was jailed, and spent many years in exile. *Allah is Not Obliged* won the 2000 Prix Renaudot, and Kourouma also wrote plays and children's books. He died in 2004.

Frank Wynne developed a passion for languages while living in Paris in the 1980s and has been a literary translator for more than a decade. *Atomised*, his translation of Michel Houellebecq's *Les Particules Élémentaires*, won the 2002 International IMPAC Dublin Literary Award, and his translation of Frédéric Beigbeder's *Windows on the World* won the 2005 Independent Foreign Fiction Prize.

Accidents

I was too small to be a soldier – too young, too weak and too scared. And the guns were far too heavy for me. Almost all our guns were Kalashnikovs – gigantic, unwieldy sub-machine guns. Pistols would have been more suitable for children like me, but there were not enough of them, thank God, or I would have been forced to shoot with them and kill someone. The jerky recoil from the Kalashnikov was so strong that I could barely fire it. None of the other smaller children could handle their Kalashnikovs either.

One day, I was busy sawing away at firewood with a knife when two boys only a year or two older than me walked past on their way to the shooting range, carrying their guns over their shoulders. The guns were so big that their butts practically reached the ground. Like all the younger children, they had to lift their guns when they climbed rocks, in order not to bang against them. There was nothing unusual in small children going off to practise shooting alone, so I did not take much notice of them.

Soon afterwards, I heard shots from the shooting range, and then one of the two children came running towards me, crying and shouting unintelligibly. His eyes were wide with horror. I dropped my knife and went up to him. His hand was wounded and bloody, and there was blood on his legs as well.

'He's dead!' he screamed. 'Dead!'

A few other people had arrived on the scene by then. They grabbed their guns and asked the boy who was dead, and where. He pointed towards the shooting range, where the rocky overhang behind the camp began. Thinking that the enemy had hidden among the rocks and killed one of our number, everyone released the safety catches on their guns in preparation for battle. Sometimes enemy soldiers had come close enough to the camp to be seen with the naked eye; there had been talk in the last few days of moving camp again soon. The problem we faced, however, was that the EPLF [Eritrean People's Liberation Front] had already hemmed us in from two directions.

I took cover and watched what happened. The boy continued crying hysterically while the others stormed off to the shooting range with their guns at the ready. But no enemy awaited them when they got there. Puzzled, they called to each other and gradually let their guns fall.

We did not seem to be under attack after all, so I emerged from my hiding place and walked over to the shooting range as well, where I practically stumbled over the boy who lay dead next to a bush. His head had been blown apart, and his body was covered in blood. I screamed, and the others ran over to me, guns at the ready. But their help had come too late – the boy had been shot dead by his best friend, as we found out later. The heavy Kalashnikov had slipped out of his grasp as he was releasing the safety catch and he had mistakenly fired the gun at his friend.

The others shrugged when they saw the body and walked back to the camp. Two of them carried the small body to a grave we had dug the day before for two soldiers killed on the front. They lifted up the stones that were lying over the grave to keep the jackals away, and threw the body in with the others. It fell with a thump like a heavy sack – there was still blood running from the boy's wounds. I stood at the edge of the grave staring into it.

'Cover him up,' one of the soldiers said to me, pressing a spade into my hands. Mechanically I shovelled sand and gravel over the body, crying all the while.

When I had finished, I turned to go back to the camp, and saw that the boy who had killed his friend had been sitting behind me all this time, perfectly still.

'He's dead,' he said, when I looked at him. 'I killed him.' He buried his face in his hands and wept.

I took him in my arms and he leaned against my shoulder as he cried. I felt like his mother, and was filled with deep sorrow, but no anger. This boy had not wanted to do what he had done. None of us was responsible for all that happened as a result of the war.

The boy rested his head in my lap. My eyes were dry at first. I felt a sense of calm at the comfort the boy was drawing from me. I had never held someone close before or had someone lean against me. I had only nestled against my grandmother, but she had not turned to me for comfort. The thought made my eyes fill with tears, which flowed unchecked.

From *Heart of Fire* by **Senait Mehari**, translated from the German by
Christine Lo (Profile Books 2006)

Senait Mehari was abandoned by her parents as a baby and spent her early
years in a state orphanage in Eritrea. When she was four her father reclaimed
her; then, at the age of six, she was sent for three years to a training camp for
child soldiers. *Heart of Fire* describes a child's view of war's brutalities, and
how she succeeded in escaping and making a new life in Germany.

Born in Asmara, the capital of Eritrea, in 1974, **Senait Mehari** grew up
during the thirty-year-war between her homeland and Ethiopia. She now
lives in Berlin where she is a well-known singer-songwriter.

Christine Lo lives in London. She has also translated *Eagles and Angels*
and *Dark Matter* by Juli Zeh. She is a judge of the Schlegel-Tieck Prize for
German translation.

The worst aspect of the Arabs' malaise is their refusal to emerge from it, but, if happiness is not in sight,some form of equilibrium at least is possible

Some people are driven to despair by the Arab malaise. They believe that the Arabs are so profoundly trapped that they will never be able to break free and, in so believing, they only make the deadlock worse. This is the extreme variant of modernism, propounded by liberals, disappointed nationalists and former activists of the left alike. Decline, according to this way of thinking, is so widespread that it damns the very notion of a renaissance: the *nahda*[†] did not just end in failure, but it was also by its very nature a historical anomaly, an impossibility right from the outset. Worse still, all attempts to free the Arabs from their predicament, particularly nationalism, are considered to have only made the problem worse. Some of these disappointed souls go so far as to internalize the culturalist distinctions that legitimize imperial domination. Their most affirmative thesis, echoing the American neoconservatives, is that change and democracy can only come from such domination, not realizing that all this will achieve is to aggravate frustrations, exacerbate victimhood and the culture of death, and thereby perpetuate the Arab malaise. For, if they are to overcome their malaise, the Arabs have no choice but to do it themselves.

Then there are those people for whom things are never better than when everything's wrong. Obviously these are the Islamist jihadists who, as good messianists, see the Arab malaise just as a bad moment to be got through – well, not as bad as all that actually, since it can be a way to gain paradise and the forty *houris* while waiting for that strange revolution which, unlike its Marxist original, is not seen as a leap into the future, but as a return to an original purity lost in the mists of time.

As a system of thought, jihadist Islamism is far from being the dominant ideology it is often portrayed as in the Western media. Yet it is powerful, no doubt because it is the only ideology that seems to offer relief from the victim status the Arabs delight in claiming (a status that in fact Islamism, jihadist or otherwise, is only too happy to confirm).

† The cultural renaissance of the nineteenth century that illuminated many Arab societies with modernity in a way that often went beyond the westernized, or westernizing, elites.

Arab victimhood goes beyond the 'Why do they hate us?' question, which Arabs would be as entitled to ask as the Americans were on the morning of September 11. Inflamed by the West's attitude to the Palestinian question, it has incorporated other elements, notably the feeling of powerlessness and also a certain crime-novel vision of history.

The cult of the victim claims that Arabs are the West's primary target, totally disregarding the other peoples of the world, and world history in general. No mention is made of Africa and its systematic pillaging; of the Americas and the genocide of the pre-Columbian populations, perpetuated in the continued marginalization of their cultures, of Indochina and its decimated generations...

Of course I am not denying what we have presupposed, that the Arabs have nothing that might compensate them for their misfortune, and that the Arab world is the only region on earth where the West has continually acted as if it were the master – and still does today, either directly or through Israel. But this doesn't change the fact that recognizing the threat to the Arab world is not the same as condoning Arab victimhood. None of the major figures of the renaissance showed any signs of indulging such a cult, nor the ideologues or practitioners of nationalism. Victims par excellence, the Palestinians avoided it in the past, and continue in a very large degree to do so, even if their situation fosters a propensity among those who helplessly look on to claim such a status.

Victimhood is the price of the defeat of the universal, rather than a product of the status quo, and its cult, served by the Arab media, in particular the much-lionized Al-Jazeera, has only been able to grow because the ideology of the moment preaches a refusal of the universal. Ideology is in fact a very grand word for the current amalgam of the fossilized remains of Arab nationalism, which, because of their age, have cut themselves off from their original, universalist sources of inspiration, and an 'Islamic nationalism' that explicitly sets out to differentiate itself from the universal, if not supplant it. Such a nationalist mishmash is not new. It was around at the end of the nineteenth century, propounded notably by Afghani. The only difference is that Afghani was a reformer of Islam, with a perfect knowledge of, and uninhibited dealings with, Western thought. The same cannot be said of his present-day successors, who abhor nothing so much as talk of religious reform.

Islamic nationalism isn't just a synonym for jihadism. It is defensive in essence, whereas jihadism can in certain lights see itself as a new conquest of the world. But the distinction between the two is nonetheless a tenuous one, and there can be no doubt that Islamic nationalism prepares the ground for jihadism. For while it may not deny the Arab malaise, as jihadism does, it nonetheless predisposes those who complain of the malaise to wallow in it, so much so that they will only replace it with something similar: the culture of death which the union of fossilized Arab nationalism and political Islam calls resistance.

There is undoubtedly an inherent explanation of the culture of death – not that it is an invariant of Islam or an essence of Arabness, but rather that, as a spectacle of endless bloodshed, it instils a self-perpetuating logic of blood for blood. If there can be no victory, then at least there can be the consolation of bloodletting – others' blood, obviously, but ours as well.

This logic may not be an invariant of Islam, but the fact remains that a religious vision of the world is at work here, even a religious vision in the sense of a system of cruelty, as Nietzsche put it. It goes without saying that this has nothing to do with the idea of sacrifice. Sacrifice has been at the root of all human conflict since the dawn of history, for the Arabs as much as anyone else, and this is the real meaning of *jihad* in the martial sense (there are also peaceful forms of *jihad*). In the twentieth century, the Palestinian fighters called themselves *fedayeen*, those ready to sacrifice their lives, like the Egyptian nationalists before them who fought the British at Suez. But in the new jihadism, death has ceased to be a potential, or even probable, price to be paid. Death has become the indispensable means to a desired end, if not an actual end in itself.

This vision of martial *jihad* incarnated in the figure of the *istishhadi*, the one who seeks martyrdom (the kamikaze, in other words), has no real antecedent in Arab–Muslim culture apart from the – non-Arab – sect of the Assassins. In the modern era, one has to wait until the Iranian revolution for its return. Shia at first, it emerged on the frontline of the Iraq–Iran war, where unbroken waves of volunteers checked the advance of the Iraqi armoured divisions before launching themselves against the Iraqi lines at the start of 1982. It appeared next in Lebanon in the form of individual suicide attacks against Western interests and the Israeli occupying forces. It should be noted that this extreme method may have been effective against the Americans, but traditional guerrilla tactics – ambushes, explosions and so on – were more decisive against the Israelis. Nonetheless other groups, some of them secular, adopted it as a model. Hezbollah gave it up when it became the only method of resistance, but kept the symbolism of blood and the totem of the *istishhadi* – a symbolism that it reinforces through the observance of Ashura. Originating in Iranian Shiism before passing to Lebanon and now Iraq, the rituals of this festival of redemptive suffering resemble certain bloody celebrations of Good Friday, in Spain for instance or the Philippines.

In principle, an insurmountable obstacle divides the Shia and the Sunni jihadists. Radical Sunni Islamism, as the doctrinal statements that have been coming out of Iraq show, holds Shia to be heretics and *rafida*, people who reject the true faith. Sunni Qur'anic literalism clearly also has its intellectual origins in South Asian Islam, notably the thought of Mawdudi, which, through the conduit of the Egyptian Sayyid Qutb, has permeated its *takfiri*, or apostatizing, strain. None of this matters, however. The martyrdom seekers first appeared in Shia circles, with the *shahids* recording their last testaments on video (the price of modernity). Furthermore, of the two Palestinian groups that have practised suicide bombing, one, Islamic Jihad, is reputed to be close to Iran, while the other, Hamas, although an offshoot of the Muslim Brotherhood, is on very good terms with Lebanese Hezbollah.

The proliferation of the culture of death and the evening-out of differences between Shias and Sunnis cannot be explained solely by the Islamization of the fight against Israel. Over and above actual events, the media, especially Al-Jazeera, have played a key role in this process, peddling a lowest-common-denominator mix of Arab nationalism and Islamic nationalism. It was doing this before September 11, defending means, justifying ends, claiming Arab victimhood. The Arab public has been systematically primed to accept the thesis of a 'clash of civilizations'.

Nonetheless, we must be able to continue rebutting Huntingdon and remembering Lévi-Strauss. If we could address the protagonists of the 'war against terror' or the 'jihad against the crusaders' in academic terms, that ought surely to be the watchword of a new universalism.

Nothing is harder than rebutting Huntingdon at a time when people are doing their utmost to cultivate difference. On the one hand, politicians and commentators constantly invoke an Eastern essentialism, even if, after long tirades opposing 'us' and 'them', they see fit to stress that Arabs and Muslims should not all be lumped in with the terrorists. On the other, there is a tendency to qualify, or even justify, the horrors of New York in terms of the evils of American politics, even if people are careful to preface their remarks with the disclaimer that the murder of innocent people goes against every precept of Islam.

We must not forget Lévi-Strauss: 'civilization', as he says, is not a category and hence cannot contain 'natural' hierarchies; and humanity is one, since it rests on a common anthropological foundation. In other words, it is as meaningless to talk of an 'attack on civilization' as it is to classify people according to their adherence to a faith, Muslim or otherwise. I should perhaps point out that supremacy isn't exclusively white. Some people in Muslim societies may be drawn to radical Islam for defensive reasons, because they feel under threat, but the rhetoric used by the warlords of radical Islamism is intentionally offensive. They justify their triumphalist proselytizing by defining the 'decadent' civilization of the Other as inferior.

So it is not just the West that needs to re-examine its stance. The Arab world in particular needs to make a profound effort to eradicate the ambiguities that encourage a logic of cultural confrontation. This means first putting victimhood into perspective. We must replace Arabs' customary assumption of victim status not by cultivating a logic of power or a spirit of revenge, but by recognizing the fact that, despite bringing defeats, the twentieth century has also brought benefits that can enable Arabs to participate in progress. Equally, we must reject the moral pragmatism lurking in the cult of the victim. If we cannot accept the powerful saying that the ends justify the means, then we can't let the victims do so either. We must not confuse terrorism with resistance, as the West confuses resistance with terrorism.

But, apart from the effects and means of confrontation, if the Arab world is to reject a clash of civilizations, then we must also give up a negative Arabocentrism (or Islamocentrism) which sees world history purely as a threat to us, and as a 'cultural', rather than political or military, threat. By the same token, we must renounce essentialist justifications of the sort that explain the silence surrounding the long affair of the Western hostages in Lebanon in the 1980s, or the indulgent attitudes towards the *fatwa* against Salman Rushdie. We must accept that democratic values are now part of humanity's shared heritage.

Such a re-examination could take place. The problem is that the elites that might push for it are caught between non-democratic regimes (frequently supported by the West, despite the 'democratic crusade' in the Middle East), on the one hand, and radical Islamism on the other. It goes without saying that the task would be easier if it was accompanied by another renaissance that had as many forms as it did inspirations, a renaissance that is still perfectly possible.

From *Being Arab* by **Samir Kassir**, translated from the Arabic by
Will Hobson (Verso 2006)

Being Arab explores what Samir Kassir describes as the 'Arab malaise,' the
political and intellectual stagnation of the Arab world. Revisiting the Arab
'golden age', the nineteenth-century flowering of Arab cultural expression
that continued into the twentieth, Kassir suggests that Arab identity has
failed to come to terms with that modernity, instead embracing pan-
Arabism and Islamism. *Being Arab* urges Arabs to reject these false
solutions and Western double standards alike, and take the future of the
region into their own hands.

Samir Kassir, one of Lebanon's best-known journalists and historians,
was assassinated by a car bomb in Beirut in June 2005. Among his books
are *A History of Beirut* and *Lebanon: An Unfinished Spring*. One of the most
prominent voices on the Arab Left, Kassir was an energetic campaigner for
the Palestinian cause and vocal critic of Syria's occupation of Lebanon.

Former Contributing Editor at Granta Books, **Will Hobson** is a critic and
translator from the French and German, whose translations include
Viramma: A Pariah's Life, Viramma (Verso); *The Battle*, Patrick Rambaud
(Picador); *Sans Moi*, Marie Desplechin (Granta); *Benares*, Barlen Pyamootoo
(Canongate); and *The Dead Man in the Bunker*, Martin Pollack (Faber). He
also translated Greenpeace's presentation to the Pope before the Kyoto
Summit into Latin.

An Afghan journey

A large open space on the edge of the city, dotted with football goals among which cows are grazing. Whimpering music from somewhere. Rolled in dust, the street children's hair sticks up in spikes, each strand turned grey with dust. Some are carrying high-heeled sandals, half-eaten flat bread or an empty canister.

I've never seen children's faces like these. They're at once childish, getting swept up in bouts of wild excitement, and at the same time old, with dark rings under their eyes and wrinkles around their mouth. Old women in children's bodies – their eyelashes mascaraed with dust. In this area of about half a square mile, they pounce on each new visitor with their shoeblack boxes and the water canisters from which they refill people's drinking bottles. Sometimes they're just curious or hoping to bag something. They might be eight years old, often younger, but they already know all about pity, shoe repairs and the art of survival.

Kabul's big stadium is hidden behind a concrete building on the other side of the field. To earn a few pennies, the children are allowed to bring water for the athletes. They bought their bread from foreign soldiers for five afghani. It's enough to ward off their own hunger for now.

These children live far away, but they see their best chance of survival in the seething city. Every morning they take the minibus for two afghani. If they can't pay they get two slaps round the face and are left behind.

'Do you know the football women who train here?'

'We've even been in their offices.'

The leader looks boldly at us. He knows all the women's and men's teams' results, he'd liked to have played himself, 'but my dad's dead, and I have to help support my family.'

We let him take us into the stadium, a ramshackle place. He watches us. 'It looks dirty to you,' he says, 'but it's paradise to me.'

In the training building two men are running circuits in a room of 25 square feet that's laid out with mats.

'They're boxers,' the little boy says, awe-struck.

Upstairs, a warm welcome from the Afghan trainer of the women's team and the German supervisor. The German is 'football crazy', his black moustache and Adidas jacket make him look like he's straight out of Germany's football scene in the Seventies. The Afghan trainer is just as enthusiastic, his friendliness floats on a deeper mourning. He travels all around the country scouting out talent, making an effort to coach in other regions too. He's just returned from the north where only half a year ago a woman was stoned. Football is an answer too.

We're led into a room that is surrounded on two sides by closed curtains, almost giving the effect of standing in a tent. It's hung with posters of the three times Women's World Footballer of the Year, Birgit Prinz, who recently led a training course for the women here. She quickly won their friendship and respect. Physically she looks like a fighting machine in comparison to the three petite, perhaps undernourished women players who now enter the room. The first has sweaty hands and an east Asian face largely covered by a veil; the second has the raw skin and red face of those who sleep outside; the third is a porcelain-fragile lady with finely drawn features and turquoise make-up, her veil has slipped and she flirts innocently. These are three of the leading women footballers, picked from the eleven clubs in Kabul who will soon be fighting it out against teams from three other Afghan provinces.

It's hoped that one day an Afghan women's national team will be formed from the group of 14–18-year-olds who are being trained together. The girls' most important quality is their ability to assert their passion for football against the doubts of society and their families. And how difficult conditions are! It's almost impossible to train at home, there's no room. In public spaces, where men can gape, they aren't allowed to play. As a result, until now none of the games have been open to the public. The girls train in full-length tracksuit trousers, but with short-sleeved shirts and without their veils.

This is a success. A few months ago they were still training in their veils, and more freedom just wouldn't be accepted yet. Now part of the burden of having women's sports accepted in public rests on the narrow shoulders of these women, in a society where women have been hidden for so long.

One of the girls trained with her brothers before registering. Now her heading skills are better than her footwork.

'And do you play hard, do you ever foul?'

'I've been fouled a lot, but never been sent off myself. Others have. They're always getting yellow cards, and sometimes red.' Every little thing that makes the game normal is a cause for celebration.

'We prefer players who have great personalities,' the trainer adds. 'A good player needs to set a good example, particularly in this unusual sport.

Also, a good player has to give her all, doing just what her trainer says.'
One of the players learnt to play in a Pakistani refugee camp. She had
been watching a game, getting really annoyed at the players, and wanted
to play herself.

'So we all chipped in for a ball, and it went from there. Two girls had
really good skills, and that spurred others on. They started playing too and
gradually we had a whole team.' She concludes like an expert: 'Because one
was good, the others got interested.'

In order to train, the girls need support from their families. Their
parents need to be brave, face ill will and help their daughters to stay
motivated. Not easy when the training is hours away – scary hours
sometimes, the journey can be dangerous. The girl that cycled for two hours
to get here today was pelted with stones and banana peel on her way.

Aggression aimed at their sport? Symptoms of war trauma? Who can
say? Everything here is watched closely – whether they wear make-up, put
on lipstick, play in shorts, take off their veils, everything is commented on.
For that reason alone the girls can only train indoors, their game improves
slowly and they feel the lack of international competitions. As tender as they
seem, they have to bear enormous psychological pressure to train. It's good
that this weekend there's a friendly game in Turkmenistan.

There's a framed photo of the FIFA president Sepp Blatter, FIFA
pennants and medals in a glass display cabinet, and a lapis lazuli globe
beside them. In some way these trophies and decorations are the insignia of
their entry into world football. How they long for public appearances, trips,
stadiums with full terraces, and yet it's so far off. I turn to the red-faced girl.
'Is your father a football fan?'

'No, he's dead. But my mother is proud. So I'm allowed to train at home
with my cousins. They throw me balls.' She has a deep, chesty cough.

It's impossible not to ask about their families, impossible to ask,
knowing that the dead wait in every answer. As they're always apologizing
for their mistakes, I try a different tack, that of the admiring chronicler with
an outsider's view of things.

'Just think,' I say. 'You're pioneers. Everything starts with you. One day
your photos will be in books. That's where Afghan women's football started,
people will say, looking at a picture on the first page of you all as you are
now. They'll say: Look at their shoes, their shirts, they still wore veils then,
and tracksuit trousers! You're preparing the path.'

They don't understand the 'path'. The future is somehow unimaginable.

Less so for the trainer. Everything depends on him, on his ability to have his way in spite of male opposition, to enthuse people, and on his resourcefulness. He tours the city's districts tirelessly, visiting families, looking out for talent and measuring the extent to which women's football can be made public.

He has a subversive strategy. Firstly the team trained in secret, then the first press releases went out. It's only been a year now that the general public has known of the existence of women's football in Afghanistan. It still needs to be convinced, just as the players' families did before they gave their approval.

'We'd do anything for our trainer,' the girls say. 'Anything. When he calls, we come, wherever we are.'

He listens to them, shows them training videos to teach them heading and dribbling. He tries to appear strict.

They get out pictures of the whole team. Pretty young women in blue and red whose faces show how much courage they need to represent this sport in public. They're sometimes intimidated by the strong reactions to what they are doing.

I talk shop with the trainer, he likes that. 'What formation do you play?'

'4-4-2. We're better attacking than in defence.'

The girls look as if they're surprised to already be part of a 'formation'. Their footballing knowledge is partial. They don't have a clear notion of the different strategies available to a team, but they look up to Ronaldinho, Ronaldo, and Michael Ballack, too.

'Who will win the World Cup?'

Two say Brazil, one Germany. What does the trainer think?

'If Germany carry on like they're playing now, they haven't got a chance.'

Sometimes the girls play against young boys from the streets of Kabul. The boys are fast and have good stamina.

'And you aren't afraid of getting fat legs from all the football?'

They giggle. 'If we were, we wouldn't have got this far. When we run onto the pitch we're prepared to lose. But we always give our best. So we can't worry about our legs.'

'Do you have any special rituals before the games?'

Do they ever. One reads certain verses of the Koran, another lights a candle and eats dried fruit, 'because you forget your problems when you're eating'. A third prays.

'And your battle cry?'

All together they shout, 'We want to work together like the fingers of a hand!'

Then they grab their handbags, proffer a friendly, if not insistent, invitation to a meal, and leave. Just 20 yards further on, at the main road, no one would suspect that the hope of Afghan football is found in these three teenagers.

—

From *An Afghan Journey* by **Roger Willemsen**, translated from the German by Stefan Tobler (Haus Publishing 2007)

Roger Willemsen is a journalist and author of many books, including a collection of interviews with former detainees after their release from the camp at Guantánamo Bay, Cuba, and also works with several relief organisations including Amnesty International and Terre des Femmes. An Afghan Journey is the result of a visit he made accompanying a friend on her return to Afghanistan after decades in exile. His focus is the lives of ordinary Afghans – women teachers, nomads, businessmen and traders, children and returnees – and the portrayal of a people more complex and determined than most Western stereotypes suggest.

Stefan Tobler was born at Belém on the edge of the Brazilian Amazon, studied Portuguese and German language and literature at Oxford University and gained a PhD in Translation from the University of East Anglia. As well as literary translation, Tobler's own writing includes cultural journalism, non-fiction and poetry.

The Yacoubian building

In 1934, Hagop Yacoubian, the millionaire and then doyen of the Armenian community in Egypt, decided to construct an apartment block that would bear his name. He chose for it the best site on Suleiman Basha and engaged a well-known Italian engineering firm to build it, and the firm came up with a beautiful design – ten lofty stories in the high classical European style, the balconies decorated with Greek faces carved in stone, the columns, steps, and corridors all of natural marble, and the latest model of elevator by Schindler. Construction continued for two whole years, at the end of which there emerged an architectural gem that so exceeded expectations that its owner requested of the Italian architect that he inscribe his name, Yacoubian, on the inside of the doorway in large Latin characters that were lit up at night in neon, as though to immortalize his name and emphasize his ownership of the gorgeous building.

The cream of the society of those days took up residence in the Yacoubian Building – ministers, big land-owning bashas, foreign manufacturers, and two Jewish millionaires (one of them belonging to the famous Mosseri family). The ground floor of the building was divided equally between a spacious garage with numerous doors at the back where the residents' cars (most of them luxury makes such as Rolls-Royce, Buick, and Chevrolet) were kept overnight and at the front a large store with three frontages that Yacoubian kept as a showroom for the silver products made in his factories. This showroom remained in business successfully for four decades, then little by little declined, until recently it was bought by Hagg Muhammad Azzam, who reopened it as a clothing store. On the broad roof two rooms with utilities were set aside for the doorkeeper and his family to live in, while on the other side of the roof fifty small rooms were constructed, one for each apartment in the building. Each of these rooms was no more than two meters by two meters in area and the walls and doors were all of solid iron and locked with padlocks whose keys were handed over to the owners of the apartments. These iron rooms had a variety of uses at that time, such as storing foodstuffs, overnight kennelling for dogs (if they were large or fierce), and laundering clothes, which in those days (before the spread of the electric washing machine) was undertaken by professional washerwomen who would do the wash in the room and hang it out on long lines that extended across the roof. The rooms were never used as places for the servants to sleep, perhaps because the residents of the building at that time were aristocrats and foreigners who could not conceive of the possibility of any human being sleeping in such a cramped place. Instead, they would set aside a room in their ample, luxurious apartments (which sometimes contained eight or ten rooms on two levels joined by an internal stairway) for the servants.

In 1952 the Revolution came and everything changed. The exodus of Jews and foreigners from Egypt started and every apartment that was vacated by reason of the departure of its owners was taken over by an officer of the armed forces, who were the influential people of the time. By the 1960s, half the apartments were lived in by officers of various ranks, from first lieutenants and recently married captains all the way up to generals, who would move into the building with their large families. General El Dakrouri (at one point director of President Muhammad Naguib's office) was even able to acquire two large apartments next door to one another on the tenth floor, one of which he used as a residence for himself and his family, the other as a private office where he would meet petitioners in the afternoon.

The officers' wives began using the iron rooms in a different way: for the first time they were turned into places for the stewards, cooks, and young maids that they brought from their villages to serve their families to stay in. Some of the officers' wives were of plebeian origin and could see nothing wrong in raising small animals (rabbits, ducks, and chickens) in the iron rooms and the West Cairo District's registers saw numerous complaints filed by the old residents to prevent the raising of such animals on the roof. Owing to the officers' pull, however, these always got shelved, until the residents complained to General El Dakrouri, who, thanks to his influence with the former, was able to put a stop to this insanitary phenomenon.

In the seventies came the 'Open Door Policy' and the well-to-do started to leave the downtown area for El Mohandiseen and Medinet Nasr, some of them selling their apartments in the Yacoubian Building, others using them as offices and clinics for their recently graduated sons or renting them furnished to Arab tourists. The result was that the connection between the iron rooms and the building's apartments was gradually severed and the former stewards and servants ceded their iron rooms for money to new, poor residents coming from the countryside or working somewhere downtown who needed a place to live that was close by and cheap.

This transfer of control was made easier by the death of the Armenian agent in charge of the building, Monsieur Grigor, who used to administer the property of the millionaire Hagop Yacoubian with the utmost honesty and accuracy, sending the proceeds in December of each year to Switzerland, where Yacoubian's heirs had migrated after the Revolution. Grigor was succeeded as agent by Maître Fikri Abd el Shaheed, the lawyer, who would do anything provided he was paid, taking, for example, one large percentage from the former occupant of the iron room and another from the new tenant for writing him a contract for the room.

The final outcome was the growth of a new community on the roof that was entirely independent of the rest of the building. Some of the newcomers rented two rooms next to one another and made a small residence out of them with all utilities (latrine and washroom), while others, the poorest, collaborated to create a shared latrine for every three or four rooms, the roof community thus coming to resemble any other popular community in Egypt. The children run around all over the roof barefoot and half-naked and the women spend the day cooking, holding gossip sessions in the sun, and, frequently, quarrelling, at which moments they will exchange the grossest insults as well as accusations touching on one another's honor, only to make up soon after and behave with complete goodwill toward one another as though nothing has happened. Indeed, they will plant hot, lip-smacking kisses on each other's cheeks and even weep from excess of sentiment and affection.

The men pay little attention to the women's quarrels, viewing them as just one more indication of that defectiveness of mind of which the Prophet – God bless him and grant him peace – spoke. These men of the roof pass their days in a bitter and wearisome struggle to earn a living and return at the end of the day exhausted and in a hurry to partake of their small pleasures – tasty hot food and a few pipes of tobacco (or of hashish if they have the money), which they either smoke in a water-pipe on their own or stay up to smoke while talking with the others on the roof on summer nights. The third pleasure is sex, in which the people of the roof revel and which they see nothing wrong with discussing frankly so long as it is of a sort sanctioned by religion. Here there is a contradiction. Any of the men of the roof would be ashamed, like most lower-class people, to mention his wife by name in front of the others, referring to her as 'Mother of So-and-so,' or 'the kids,' as in 'the kids cooked mulukhiya today,' the company understanding that he means his wife. This same man, however, will feel no embarrassment at mentioning, in a gathering of other men, the most precise details of his private relations with his wife, so that the men of the roof come to know almost everything of one another's sexual activities. As for the women, and without regard for their degree of religiosity or morality, they all love sex enormously and will whisper the secrets of the bed to one another, followed, if they are on their own, by bursts of laughter that are carefree or even obscene. They do not love it simply as a way of quenching lust but because sex, and their husbands' greed for it, makes them feel that despite all the misery they suffer they are still women, beautiful and desired by their menfolk. At that certain moment when the children are asleep, having had their dinner and given praise to their Lord, and there is enough food in the house to last for a week or more, and there is a little money set aside for emergencies, and the room they all live in is clean and tidy, and the husband has come home on Thursday night in a good mood because of the effect of the hashish and asked for his wife, is it not then her duty to obey his call, after first bathing, prettying herself up, and putting on perfume? Do these brief hours of pleasure not furnish her with proof that her wretched life is somehow, despite everything, blessed with success? It would take a skilled painter to convey to us the expressions on the face of a woman on the roof of a Friday morning, when, after her husband has gone down to perform the prayer and she has washed off the traces of love-making, she emerges to hang out the washed bedding – at that moment, with her wet hair, her flushed complexion, and the serene expression in her eyes, she looks like a rose that, watered with the dew of the morning, has arrived at the peak of its perfection.

—

From *The Yacoubian Building* by **Alaa Al-Aswany**, translated from the Arabic by Humphrey Davies (Fourth Estate 2007)

Alaa Al-Aswany's simultaneous celebration and dissection of a society dominated by bribery and corruption polarised reactions when it was published in Egypt. Religious feelings live side by side with promiscuity; bribery and exploitation alternate with moments of joy and elation; modernity clashes with visions, sometimes militant, of a more ancient society.

　　Alaa Al-Aswany, born in 1957, is a dentist by profession and for many years practised in the Yacoubian Building. His novel *Chicago* and a collection of short stories, *Friendly Fire*, are also published in English, and he has written prolifically for Egyptian newspapers on politics, literature and social issues.

Humphrey Davies is an award-winning translator from Arabic. He has translated works by Naguib Mahfouz, Alaa Al-Aswany, Ahmed Alaidy, Gamal Al-Ghitani and Ahlam Mosteghanemi. He also translated the Arab Booker Award-winning novel *Sunset Oasis* by Bahaa Taher.

Touba and the meaning of night

She was no more than six or seven years old when the Englishman came to their home. Never had anyone seen an Englishman, never had an Englishman come to anyone's home. But he came to Adib's home. Only much later did she realize the significance of the event.

Earlier, the Englishman had been galloping his horse down the dusty street when her father had begun to cross. The English horse had shied, and Adib had fallen down right in front of it. The Englishman struck Adib on the face with his whip and in broken Persian cried, 'Stupid fool!' and galloped away. Asdolah the butcher had been chopping meat on a tree stump in front of his shop. Ten steps behind, he tried to catch up to the Englishman, his chopping knife still in hand, cursing the man as loudly as he could. Unsuccessful, he returned to help the other shopkeepers lift Adib from the dust and the mud, and to stare in amazement at the reddened whip mark on his face. This incident was to become a torment to Adib, a memory that would not leave him for the rest of his life. The shopkeepers surrounding Haji Adib stared at him expectantly. If Haji had given the order, they undoubtedly would have gone on a rampage. Haji Adib never gave the order, and he never gave an explanation either. At the time of the accident, Haji Adib had been lost in thought, solving one of Mullah Sadra's great philosophical propositions of Transcendent Theosophy. Because he was thinking about sitting in discussion with his friends that night, he had not noticed the horse.

Now that his thoughts had returned to the street, he noticed the people gazing at him. He also felt the burning of his left eye, reddened by the Englishman's whip. He wanted to cover his eye with a handkerchief to stop the cold wind from causing him pain, but he could not do so in front of the people. In a loud voice he said that he would show the Englishman such retaliation that it would be written down in the stories. Filled with determination, he started walking. The shopkeepers followed him silently, but also with determination. After five or six steps, he turned around and assured everyone that the Englishman would be whipped there and in front of them, but now it was best that they return to their work. He walked away quickly, and his anger grew deeper within him with every step.

By the time he arrived at Moshir O-Doleh's home he was flushed with rage. Moshir O-Doleh's servant was shocked by the unannounced arrival of the guest, and in such an extraordinary state. The servant directed Adib to the parlor. There, Adib's anger gradually turned to a confused agony over the whole situation.

The room in which Adib sat was furnished in European style. All around the room were various easy chairs and other fringed furniture. Paintings depicting scenes of Swiss mountains and European cities hung on the walls. The house had electricity, and it glowed with the light of immense crystal chandeliers. It truly belonged to someone with the name Doleh, which was a title given to those affiliated with the government. Haji seated himself on the edge of one of the upholstered chairs. Numbness and exhaustion overcame him as he waited.

His host finally arrived, apologized for his delay, and the two men drank tea and ate some pastries. Adib was beside himself. Though he searched for words to describe the event, he did not feel he could demean himself by complaining as the peasants did. But neither was he a warrior who could go out and claim what was his right. He explained to his host that their country and the fundamental and constitutional rights of the people were in the hands of the great men, a segment of whom were educated. If these men did not exist, then the wheels would stop turning, the peasants would grow impatient, and chaos would reign.

Moshir O-Doleh listened to him with great interest and agreed with everything he said. With a sense of degradation and humiliation, Adib continued by recounting the story of the Englishman. It was with great difficulty that he overcame the trembling in his hands and his voice. He was trying to say that he considered himself neither great nor important, but if he could be whipped by an Englishman, in front of enemies and friends alike – he, who carried the robe and turban of an educated man – then what would the people think? What could happen?

Moshir O-Doleh must have realized the significance of the problem, for his anger was now as deep as Haji Adib's. He spoke with resounding rhetoric, and in the end he promised to bring the incident to the attention of His Majesty Mozafar O-Din Shah, and to pursue the English culprit through the British ambassador and give him his due. He added that things like this should not happen at the threshold of the twentieth century.

On his way back home, Haji Adib recounted his visit with Moshir O-Doleh to the shopkeepers in the street, emphasizing that they would soon see the results. He had calmed down by the time he arrived home at sunset.

The Englishman came the following week. The day before his arrival, European furniture was delivered to Haji Adib's home, with no prior notice.

Moshir O-Doleh's secretary apologetically explained that Europeans were not used to sitting on the floor. And it would not be appropriate for the Haji Adib to sit on the floor with the Englishman's head higher than his own.

He also reported that, while His Excellency Moshir O-Doleh sent his regards, he wanted to mention respectfully that the culprit was not an Englishman but a Frenchman. His Excellency had been very diligent in trying to find the Englishman through the British Embassy, but to no avail. Then another Englishman told him that a Frenchman had been heard reciting the story of the incident. His Excellency pursued the matter through the French Embassy, and the culprit was found. Nevertheless, the European culprit continued to be called the Englishman, even by the secretary himself.

The Englishman was coming to apologize personally to Haji Adib. In expectation of his arrival, twenty-four hours of absolute frenzy reigned in the old-fashioned house. To make things a little easier, Moshir O-Doleh sent his personal servant, who was familiar with serving Westerners, in order to make sure that no mistake would occur.

Haji Adib's wife, Touba, and the younger children, together with the maid, Morvarid, were all seated behind the curtain that separated the living room from the salon so that they could view the Englishman. As Haji walked back and forth in the living room, he heard a knocking at the front gate. Moshir O-Doleh's servant opened the door and directed the Englishman to the salon.

The man wore a riding suit, and the spurs on his boots made loud metallic sounds. He had blue eyes and colorless skin, and his hair was blond. Haji's wife turned instinctively to look at Touba. She wanted to know if her daughter's hair was lighter than the Englishman's. Touba had been born with blond hair and was different in this respect from all her brothers and sisters. The Englishman's hair was lighter. In fact, his hair was golden, while hers was more of a strawberry blond. The child paid no attention to these matters. She was totally absorbed in the Englishman.

The servant poured tea, then signaled for Haji to enter. Haji drew aside the curtain between the two rooms, and the Englishman stood up and bent his head slightly. He smiled and stretched his hand toward Haji. Haji shook his hand in a Western manner. Then the two men sat facing each other.

The Englishman gave a brief speech in his own language – not one word of which was comprehensible to Haji Adib, who had no alternative but to listen through to the end with a smile. The absence of a translator was deeply felt. Haji Adib assumed that the Englishman was asking his forgiveness. In response, Haji Adib uttered a few distracted sentences of understanding and forgiveness while staring at the man's riding boots, which somehow defiled the carpet. At the same time, he looked at his own bare feet. He had not thought of putting on shoes for the Englishman. He considered the Englishman's act bold, though he had, in this very brief time, come to learn a few of their customs. He was wavering between viewing this act as a new insult or disregarding it, when suddenly the Englishman rose, took a small box out of his pocket, and stepped toward Haji to put the box in his hands. Haji Adib stared at the box with amazement and turned questioning eyes toward the Englishman. The man spoke, gesturing to Haji Adib that he should open the box. Haji Adib removed the cover and found a ring with a large diamond in it. The Englishman apparently had said that the ring was a gift for the lady of the house, but Haji Adib, not comprehending a word, looked at it in bewilderment. The sparkling glow of the diamond caught the eyes of Haji's wife, and she involuntarily pinched her daughter's back.

Haji Adib wanted to return the present. He uttered some words refusing the gift. The Englishman could not understand and merely smiled. Finally, Haji Adib also had to gesture. He put the ring to his lips and kissed it, then touched it to his forehead. In his mind, this was the way to show his gratitude. Then he stood up and put the box on the Englishman's knees, and repeated, 'No, no! Never! It is impossible!' The Westerner seemed to understand some of the words. He tried to return the present to Haji Adib, but Haji Adib again adamantly refused. The man put the box in his pocket and shrugged his shoulders. It was time to go. He stood up, spoke a few words, bent his head slightly. They shook hands again, and the Englishman departed.

The shopkeepers had gathered around the arched entry where the Englishman had tethered his horse. They watched him bend his head to avoid hitting the door frame as he exited, and their eyes followed him as he calmly led the horse away from Haji's undistinguished house. The people whispered among themselves as the Englishman calmly mounted his horse and rode away at a walk, disappearing at the end of the alley.

The next couple of hours at Haji Adib's home were spent entertaining the neighborhood and recounting details of the visit. The part about the diamond and Haji Adib's rejection of it was very well received. However, that night Haji Adib's wife nagged at him. She could not forget the glow of the diamond. Haji Adib, who never shouted, now screamed. How could he possibly accept a gift from someone who had lashed him with a riding whip? But the woman sulked, and a week passed before husband and wife spoke to each other again.

From *Touba and the Meaning of Night* by **Shahrnush Parsipur**,
translated from the Persian by Havva Houshmand and Kamran Talattof
(Marion Boyars 2007)

After her father dies when she is only fourteen, Touba – intelligent but
barely educated – proposes marriage to a 52-year-old man who originally
proposed to her mother. She divorces him a few years later and marries
a Qajar prince, but when he takes a second wife she also divorces him.
Alone and impoverished, weaving carpets to make money and care for
her children, she seeks spiritual truth but ultimately the demands of her
crumbling household and family dramas including abortion, secret
marriage, murder and extremism intervene.

    Shahrnush Parsipur attended the University of Tehran and worked as
a producer for Iranian national television. Protesting about the execution
of two poets in 1974, she was imprisoned, and in 1980 was again gaoled,
for four years. On her release she started writing, and *Touba and the
Meaning of Night* became a bestseller. She now lives in San Francisco.

Havva Houshmand taught at the National University of Iran for twelve
years and is currently a faculty member at the Albuquerque TVI
Community College in the USA, teaching humanities and cultural studies.
She is the founder of a consulting partnership, Culture Alive, offering
workshops and counselling with emigrants.

Kamran Talattoff is Professor in the Department of Near Eastern Studies
at the University of Tuscon, Arizona. He is co-translator of *Women Without
Men* by Shahrnush Parsipur and the author of many articles on Persian
studies and Iranian political figures.

Illusions [Fr]

et nous avons cru nous retrouver
sur une terre d'asile
pendant que d'autres
tapis dans la pénombre
de toutes les frontières
ciraient déjà leurs bottes
presque neuves
mais tu ne le savais pas encore

tu rêvais d'une ville où les oiseaux
font leur nid au bord de toutes les fenêtres
tu rêvais pendant que d'autres
déjà en marche
pressaient le pas pour piétiner
les fleurs de ton jardin
arrosées de ton sang
mais tu ne le savais pas encore

tu t'apprêtais à rejoindre
la foule en liesse
pendant que d'autres
franchissaient par colonnes entières
les portes de la ville

et quand il t'a semblé entendre
leurs bottes
presque neuves
résonner sur l'asphalte fumant
il était déjà trop tard

Illusions [En]

and we thought we were back together again
in a land of asylum
while others
lurking in the shadows
of all the frontiers
were already waxing
their nearly new boots
but you didn't know it yet

you were dreaming of a city where birds
make their nests by every window
you were dreaming while others
were already marching
eager to trample over
the flowers in your garden
watered with your blood
but you didn't know it yet

you were getting ready to join
the jubilant crowd
while whole columns
of others
were pouring through the city gates

and when you thought you heard
their nearly new boots
resounding
on the smoking tarmac
it was already too late

Un été original [Fr]

1   on m'a volé mon été
pendant que je voyais passer les hirondelles

dites!
avez-vous une cigarette?

– il reste la mer
la douce brise du soir
le ciel bleu d'Alger
et les jolies filles
ivres de soleil –

2   je voudrais tant m'étendre
sur un lit de sable – me laisser aimer
par les odeurs d'iode et d'algues –
et si une madone me brûle les yeux
me consume le cœur d'un regard
où les cils battent au ralenti
je sourirai
'permettez... vous êtes si belle!'

3   dans les quartiers résidentiels
d'Alger-chimères
on danse
la main dans la main
au rythme des coups de reins
dans la nuit travestie

et on danse
et on boit
à la santé du passé
à l'avenir aussi
quand grillent sur la braise

An original summer [En]

1   they stole my summer
while I was watching the swallows fly

hey!
have you got a cigarette?

– the sea remains
the evening's gentle breeze
the blue sky of Algiers
and the pretty girls
drunk on sunshine –

2   I'd so like to stretch out
on a bed of sand – let the smells
of iodine and seaweed love me –
and if some madonna burns my eyes
consumes my heart with a look
through slowly beating lashes
I'll smile
'forgive me... you're so beautiful!'

3   in the residential districts
of dream-Algiers
they dance
hand in hand
to the rhythm of pelvic thrusts
the transvestite night away

and they dance
and they toast
the health of the past
and the future too
while animals on spits

des bêtes embrochées
dans les niches
les chiens bergers
attendent
les restes des gigots
et les caniches
s'amusent
sur les genoux
des dames
qui bavent

4   je veux manger du foie
des crevettes
des ananas
faire du ski et de la planche à voile

hier encore
le boucher m'a regardé de travers
en me servant une demi-livre
de chat
dans du papier journal
– c'était la première page
et le président y paraissait très fier –

dites!
avez-vous une cigarette ?

5   un jour j'ai connu une fille
– elle était maigre –
je l'ai rencontrée chez un libraire
qui vendait aussi de la *zlabia*
pendant le ramadan

nous avons marché sous le soleil d'août
pendant trois heures ensuite
nous sommes allés voir un film
de chez nous

grill over the coals
in the kennels
alsatians
wait
for remains of legs of lamb
and poodles
amuse themselves
on the knees
of drooling
ladies

4   I want to eat liver
prawns
pineapples
try windsurfing and skiing

only yesterday
the butcher gave me a dirty look
as he served me half a pound
of cat
wrapped in newspaper
– it was the front page
and the president looked very proud –

hey!
have you got a cigarette?

5   one day I got to know a girl
– she was skinny –
I met her in a bookseller's shop
he was also selling *zlabia*
during ramadan

then we walked under the August sun
for three hours
we went to see a film
one of our own

les rafales de mitraillettes
'Dieu est le plus grand !'
'Fellaga!'
(il est mort)
'Gloire à nos martyrs!'
les you-you
les drapeaux
en noir et blanc

elle était toute drôle
les cheveux ébouriffés
et la bouche comme une fraise écrasée

trois ans durant ou cinq ou dix
nous avons marché sous le soleil
nous passions inaperçus

6   comme tous les gentlemen
d'Alger-trottoir
j'attends

mais il reste la mer
la douce brise du soir
le ciel bleu d'Alger
et mon amour interdit

bursts of machinegun fire
'God is the greatest!'
'Fellaga!'
(he's dead)
'Glory to our martyrs!'
the *you-yous*
the flags
in black and white

she was all odd
hair dishevelled
mouth like a squashed strawberry

for three full years or five or ten
we walked under the sun
we passed unnoticed

6   like all the gentlemen
of sidewalk-Algiers
I'm waiting

but the sea remains
the evening's gentle breeze
the blue sky of Algiers
and my forbidden love

From *State of Emergency* by **Soleïman Adel Guémar**, translated from the French by Tom Cheesman and John Goodby (Arc 2007)

Soleïman Adel Guémar was born and grew up in Algiers, but after working as a journalist and winning two national poetry prizes was forced to leave Algeria in 2002 to seek safety for himself and his family in the United Kingdom.

    State of Emergency, a selection of Guémar's poetry, is rooted in Algerian experience, speaking of life's sensual pleasures in the face of morbid and grotesque political repression. In her introduction Lisa Appignanesi writes: 'This volume marks an important moment: a record from the inside of a history which is too palpably of our times.'

Tom Cheesman lectures in German at Swansea University. In 2003 he founded non-profit Hafan Books to publish writing by refugees and asylum seekers, alongside work by other writers in Wales. His poetry translations include Manfred Peter Hein's *Between Winter and Winter*.

John Goodby lectures in English at Swansea University, specializing in Irish and Welsh writing in English. His poetry publications include *A Birmingham Yank* and an experimental translation of Heinrich Heine's *Germany: A Winter's Tale*.

The loser

Vilma was the apple of Xhoda's eye. The lap dog was the apple of Vilma's eye. I decided to poison Vilma's dog.

I poisoned Vilma's white lap dog to take revenge. There wasn't any other reason for doing it. As a child, I considered myself equal to all the other kids in the sense of social equality, or rather, to the extent a twelve-year-old can understand the concept of social equality. I'm sure that I had no complexes and didn't see myself as descending from a race of mongrels – as belonging to a species of wretches – and I didn't see Vilma as stemming from a race of lap dogs – a species of the chosen few. It was only later that I'd learn that Vilma and I belonged to different species. This was to be my second trauma. But at the time, I was still under the influence of the first trauma when, after the beating, I lost all respect for my father. Vilma's puppy would have to pay, even if it meant that Vilma would be in tears for days and nights on end and that Xhoda would rage and lose his mind.

It was a beautiful lap dog, and like all others of its kind it would rush out and bark wildly, sticking its nose through the pickets of the fence whenever anyone walked by. It barked at me that way, too. It was a warm afternoon and Vilma was sitting in her little chair near the stairs, concentrating on her book. She didn't look up when the barking started. But since I didn't budge, it started lunging at me furiously, yelping loud enough to wake up the whole neighbourhood. I'd counted on this. Annoyed, Vilma finally raised her head. Her eyes caught mine... and mine caught hers. They were azure blue like the ocean. We recognised one another, but we'd never spoken because we'd always been in different classes at school. And, to tell the truth, I really had no desire to speak to Vilma right then.

First she frowned and then shouted something like 'Max, be quiet, get back here!' As Max had no intention of obeying, she got up, tossed her book on the chair, and ran towards us. I stood there bewildered. Max only calmed down when his mistress picked him up. I blushed and attempted a smile. I told her she had a beautiful dog. 'Don't say that,' replied Vilma. 'He'll get all stuck-up if he hears you and he'll start biting everyone who walks past the house.'

All of a sudden I turned and bolted. Vilma stood there at the fence with Max. Years later, she reminded me of the scene. 'You were so strange, the way you stared at me, looking right into my eyes! I went back to the stairs with Max and pretended I was reading, but actually I was waiting for you to come back and stare into my eyes again. No boy had ever looked at me that way and I didn't understand what it was that made me wait for you. I never stopped believing that you'd reappear at the fence one day, even later when you were going to university and rumours had spread in town that you were having an affair with a widow. But you never turned up. I waited for you, even though you poisoned my Max. I cried for him as I would have for a brother. And yet, I waited for you, though I was convinced you'd never come back.'

From the moment I started to run, I was convinced, too, that I wouldn't go back. When Vilma picked Max up and started to talk to me, I knew that if I stayed any longer, I wouldn't be able to take revenge at all. I don't know how to explain it properly, but I felt that if I hung around near Vilma, listening to her voice, looking into her eyes and watching her pet the dog, I wouldn't feel up to poisoning Max. And if I didn't poison Max, Vilma wouldn't cry. And if Vilma didn't cry, Xhoda wouldn't lose his mind.

Max had a painful but quick end. Before we committed the crime, Sherif asked me to find out what food the dog preferred. With some trouble, I found out from a boy who used to visit Vilma quite often – they were cousins – that Max loved fried liver, preferably lamb. I got some. Without his father noticing, Sherif mixed it with the poison used to exterminate wild dogs. We did away with Max one afternoon while Vilma was taking him out for a walk, as she often did, to the edge of town where the fields start. Sherif reported to me that it was no problem getting the dog to eat the bait while Vilma was busy talking to a girlfriend. Max gave up the ghost almost instantly. Right after, everything spun out of control.

Sherif came over the next evening. He'd never been to my house and when I saw him leaning against the banister in the stairwell, I suspected something had happened. Another thing worried me, too. Sherif hadn't turned up for school that day. He looked scared and asked me to come out so that we could talk somewhere in private where we wouldn't be seen or heard. It was dark, so we managed to get through the centre of town without being seen and reached the neighbourhood near the riverbank. We crouched there in the bushes. Sherif was shaking and started to cry. Then I understood what had happened. A state of emergency had been declared in town the moment word of Max's demise spread. 'After lunch,' Sherif explained, 'the headmaster came over with two policemen. I don't know what they talked about outside, but my dad came back into the house furious and clenched his fist at me. He made a threat: 'I'll kill you with my own bare hands if I ever find out that you were involved in this business.'

Poor Sherif was frightened to death. He was sure that his father was going to kill him. But this was nothing compared to another even more terrifying aspect. Even though Sherif hadn't gone to school that day, Fagu and his gang were able to find him down by the river. Everyone suspected Sherif. They beat him up and said they'd murder him if he didn't tell them the truth. Sherif denied everything. It was the fact that he'd denied the whole affair that made his position so precarious. No one believed him, including his father and Fagu. Now, with tears in his eyes, he kissed my hand (I'll never forget how he bent over to kiss it) and begged me to save him. Otherwise he'd have no choice but to throw himself into the river and drown.

I didn't need time to think about it. Sherif was petrified. I'd got him involved in the affair, so I was obligated to do something. I had to assume responsibility, and that's what I did. Not because I was afraid that he would actually kill himself, although, given the circumstances, I believed he could have. I decided to admit to being the perpetrator of the crime because I felt that I could stand the torments of hell better than his slobbery kisses on my hand. If I didn't own up, Sherif would come around every day and lick my hand like a beaten dog.

I confessed to Fagu. This way, I was sure the news would be spread instantly in the right direction and yet I'd have enough time to prepare myself for the inevitable. Fagu glared at me. It was the most incredible thing he'd ever heard. He only believed me when I explained to him that I'd committed the murder to take revenge on Xhoda. Everyone knew that Xhoda had beaten me up recently. So vengeance would be seen as justified, even in this form. Fagu couldn't touch me personally. If he did, he'd be in trouble himself. None of the tough guys in his gang would have forgiven him for beating me up just for Vilma's sake.

Events took their course. Fagu, at that time, was bigger than I was, and, most definitely stronger, too. He foamed at the mouth, but just sneered at me and left. From that day on, my life became unbearable. Everyone stared at me as if I were a criminal. At school, when we were lined up in the courtyard, what I'd done was denounced as the most dastardly event ever to have taken place in that town. My grade for behaviour was reduced by two marks and I was suspended from school for three days. My first caning didn't come from Xhoda, who didn't even deign to call me into his office, but from my father. I wasn't expecting it because he'd never beaten me before. The beating happened when he got back from the police station where he'd been summoned to account for my behaviour. I also discovered that he'd paid compensation to Xhoda, an amount of around three or four thousand leks. To this very day, I don't know if my father beat me because of the crime itself, because of the money he was forced to pay or because of the dread he felt all through his body when he was called to the police station. Whatever the reason, from that time on, my father acquired a taste for caning me. He learned how to beat me, but I also learned how to take a beating. Once you get used to it, nothing else makes much of an impression.

That pine tree had been thirty years younger and I was so thin that I could hide behind it. Vilma was sitting in her chair reading a book. I'd been watching her for over an hour and she hadn't raised her head even once. There was no Max to rush out and bark by the fence. He was dead. I stood there cringing behind the trunk of the pine tree. I was sure that Vilma knew I was there. I was lost in thought when suddenly I felt something at my feet. I picked it up. It was a stone wrapped in paper. 'Are you sorry for what you did? Is that what you've come to tell me? Don't even bother. You've been hiding behind that tree for five days now, like a robber. Even if you say you're sorry, I won't forgive you. Why Max? What did Max ever do to you? Even if you have an answer, I know that I'll always hate you.'

When I looked up, the chair where Vilma had been sitting was empty. This is the last vision of my childhood that I can recall. Everything else is gone. All that's left is the empty chair, as if to remind me of the emptiness of my existence.

From *The Loser* by **Fatos Kongoli**, translated from the Albanian by
Robert Elsie and Janice Mathie-Heck (Seren 2007)

The Loser portrays not only the suppression of art by a controlled press
and the mechanisms of the state, but of a people denied the freedom to
express themselves individually. An apparently grim narrative about the
misfortunes of one man – a lonely childhood, a disgraced family member,
a dalliance with politics and a fall from grace, the failure of a forbidden
affair – this is also a moving and blackly funny novel of love and loss.

Fatos Kongoli was born in the central Albanian town of Elbasan and
grew up in Tirana. He chose not to publish during the Hoxha dictatorship
but devoted his energies to a career as a mathematician. There was, as he
later noted in an interview, 'no Marxist strategy for mathematics'. His
talent emerged in the 1990s, revealing a classic example of a writer whose
work and expression were silenced by a totalitarian regime.

Robert Elsie is a Canadian with a longstanding specialism in Albanian
and Balkan history and literature. He has translated dozens of novels
and stories and runs the website 'Albanian Authors in Translation',
which includes the largest selection of Albanian and Kosovan literature
in English. He is currently employed as an interpreter by The Hague
International Courts, where he translated at the trial of Slobodan Milosevic.

Janice Mathie-Heck is a Canadian teacher, poet, translator, editor and
literary critic. She has collaborated with Robert Elsie in translating and
editing Albanian literature.

The long corridors of the women workers' hostel

A new life began with the communist hostel warden. Before he came, there had only been women in the hossel. The women searched for their mothers, their sisters or their stepmothers in the other women, and like sheep who on a rainy night were afraid of thunder and lightning, they came too close to one another and sometimes squeezed one another until they couldn't breathe. Now we had a shepherd, who could sing. He gave us books and said: 'Here, I'm giving you my best friend.' One of his best friends was Chekhov. So he was not the only man we had. Other men came into our hossel with him: Dostoevsky, Gorky, Jack London, Tolstoy, Joyce, Sartre and one woman, Rosa Luxemburg. I didn't know any of them before. Some women fetched books from him, which perhaps they didn't read, but they loved these books as a child loves foreign stamps, they loved to have these books in their bags when they got on the bus to the radio valve factory.

When our communist hostel warden spoke to a woman, he always began his sentences with the word 'Sugar'. When he spoke to several women at once, he said 'Sugars'. 'Sugars, go and sit down, I'll be with you in a moment', 'Sugar, here's a letter for you'. The women who loved him also began to address each other as 'Sugar' and 'Sugars'. And so slowly the hossel divided into the women who said 'Sugar' and the women who didn't say 'Sugar'. When the women in the kitchen were cooking with the pots and pans, the pots and pans were also divided between the women who addressed one another as 'Sugar' and those who didn't address one another as 'Sugar'. After they'd finished cooking, those who said 'Sugar' to one another gave the pots to the women who also said 'Sugar' to them, and those who didn't say 'Sugar' gave the pots to those who didn't say 'Sugar'. The women who said 'Sugar' found the evening. After the factory work they didn't immediately go into the night any more. So the hossel divided once more into the women who had their evenings and the women who immediately leapt over the evening into the night. When these women went to bed, the audience was slowly making its way into the Hebbel Theatre, which was opposite our hossel. The others began to draw out their evenings. They bought records, and so Beethoven's 9th Symphony came into the hossel and a hit song: 'Junge, komm bald wieder' – 'Boy, come back soon'. In the hossel lounge the TV was on in the background, and they listened back to back without a break to the Beethoven and 'Boy, come back soon', as if, were they to remain without these sounds and voices for one second, the

evening would disappear from their hands again. It was so loud that sometimes even our communist hostel warden shouted: 'Donkeys, lie down! Donkeys, go to sleep!' The women who didn't say 'Sugar' did, however, use his new word 'Donkey' and now shouted from their rooms to the hossel salon: 'Donkeys, lie down!' We three girls also belonged to the donkeys. Even the morning bus, which took us to the factory, divided into two groups of women. The women who didn't say 'Sugar' but 'Donkeys, lie down!' now sat down as a group at the front of the bus, and those who said 'Sugar' and were donkeys sat at the back of the bus. In the factory, however, everyone
sat at their old place. Those who drew out their evenings and so stole something from the night often went to the toilet in the factory, the lens in front of their right eye. Behind the lens our right eye now looked even sleepier than our left. In the toilet room we went on buying cigarettes for ten pfennigs from the German women workers and went to the toilet with the cigarette. When we went to the toilet, we often forgot to take our lenses out of our right eye, so our cigarettes, which we smoked in the toilet, looked much bigger. We smoked inside and nodded off a little. However, Frau Missel, the forewoman, came and fetched us out of the toilet. So slowly,
even in the factory, the women divided into those who slept in the toilet and those who didn't sleep in the toilet.

At some point Beethoven's 9th Symphony and 'Boy, come back soon' were no longer enough to draw out the evenings. The women who were donkeys now went out of the hossel. From that day on, the automatic light in the hallway of the house constantly went on and off and the hossel door opened and shut with a loud creak. We three youngest girls of the women's hossel walked along the streets of Berlin to Zoo Station, to Aschinger, and there we had pea soup and no longer the horse meatballs from our snack bar next to the offended station. But we went on talking loudly when we passed our telephone box next to our offended railway station, so that our parents in Turkey could hear us. On some evenings, when we three girls came back late to our hossel room from Zoo-Aschinger and in the night filed our nails with a file, another woman, who was already in bed, threw her pillow at us and shouted at us: 'You'll end up whores!' I went on practising my German sentences, which I didn't understand, at the newspaper display case every morning, and replied to the pillow with newspaper headlines learned by heart:

THE GLOVES ARE OFF
LOOKING COSTS MORE
SOVIETS ARE ONLY ONLOOKERS

When we walked along the Berlin streets, I was astonished at how few men were to be seen on the streets, even in the evenings there were not many men to be seen. I was also astonished that the men whom I saw didn't scratch themselves between the legs, like many Turkish men on Turkish streets. And some men carried the bags of the women they were walking beside and looked as if they were not married to these women, but to these bags.

They walked along the streets as if at that moment they were being filmed for TV. To me the streets and people were like a film, but I didn't have a part in this film. I saw the people, but they didn't see us. We were like the birds, who flew somewhere and from time to time came down to earth, before flying away again.

We had all come here only for a year, after a year we all wanted to go back. When we looked at ourselves in the mirror, no mother, no father, no sister walked past in the room behind us. In the mirror our mouths no longer talked to a mother or sister. We no longer heard their voices, the whispering of their clothes, their laughter in front of the mirror, so we saw ourselves every day in the mirror as lonely people.

Once we had understood in the mirror that we were alone, everything was easier. So we three girls went to the Wienerwald restaurant on Ku'damm and ate half-chicken. Then I saw Christ. To warm up, we had gone into a church, and there for the first time I saw Christ on the cross. In Istanbul, too, Christ was one of our prophets. I loved him as a child, but I had heard nothing of the cross, my grandmother had told me that as a baby Christ floated alone in a basket on a river. I also loved his mother Meryem.

In the factory we went on smoking Stuyvesant in the toilet and falling asleep there, the forewoman, Frau Missel, fetched us out again, the faulty radio valves landed in the bin. When there were too many radio valves in the bin, we bought perfume, soap and creams from the men who came with suitcases during the factory breaks. We also signed documents, without knowing that these were encyclopedia subscriptions, the money was deducted from our monthly wage. We thought that the forewoman, Frau Missel, would be less angry because of the broken radio valves if we bought the things.

One day we three girls went into a pub for the first time. It was snowing outside. Men were standing at the bar. The men asked in English: 'Where are you from?' Rezzan and I could speak some English, and Rezzan replied: 'From the North Pole, we are Eskimos, our sledges are outside.'

When the other women came back to the hossel at night, they also brought back new addresses from Berlin with them: KaDeWe, Café Keese, Café Kranzler. So we three girls went to Café Keese. Telephone dance. There were telephones on the tables, one could invite men to dance. We sat down at two tables and phoned each other. 'Hello, Mother, I'm your daughter, how are you?' – 'Oh, my child, how are you? What have you been eating?' – 'Meatballs, mother.' Then a German man called us. 'Dance?' We replied with what we had learned from our communist hostel warden in the German lessons: 'Remember me to my father.' The next morning the women who had found their evenings and gone out of the hossel were told by the other women: 'You are whores and go to other factory hossels, where Turkish men live, you spread the semen of these men on your bread and eat it.' So once again the women's hossel divided into the women who spread Turkish men's semen on their bread and ate it, and the women who spread margarine on their bread and ate it.

But we didn't know any Turkish men yet. We knew only our communist hostel warden. Soon, however, some women got to know quite a different side of Turkish men. The women came from the night shift, the men stood at the bus stop at night and struck the most beautiful woman in the face. It was dark, none of the women saw the men properly, they only heard their voices: 'Whores, what are you doing here in the night?' After that the communist hostel warden went to the bus stop every night and met the women who were coming from the night shift.

Then a man came into the hossel after all. One night outside the hossel door we found a man lying on the ground in the snow. His trouser buttons were undone, and he wasn't wearing any underpants. He had peed himself. Upstairs the whole women's hossel was asleep, and we three girls tried to help the man to his feet. He did stand up, but went to the middle of the road and sat down in the snow again. We thought the cars would run him over. So we brought the man into the hossel lounge, laid him on a couch and went to sleep. In the morning the man was still lying on the couch, asleep, smiling in his sleep, and a stiff penis stuck out of his trousers when the women switched on the light. 'The three girls are rabid,' said the women to one another, 'we will go to factory boss Herschering.' The Dove, the wife of our communist hostel warden, was supposed to translate their sentences for Schering. The communist hostel warden listened to them, then he spoke to the women who wanted to go to Herschering. For the first time he began his sentences not with 'Sugar' or 'Sugars', but said: 'Children.' This word silenced the women. The communist hostel warden gathered us all in the hossel lounge, addressed some women now as 'Children', others as 'Sugar' or 'Sugars' and redistributed the women in the rooms. Now the children lived with children, sugars with sugars, donkeys with donkeys, whores with whores.

—

From *The Bridge of the Golden Horn* by **Emine Sevgi Özdamar**, translated from the German by Martin Chalmers (Serpent's Tail 2007)

The Bridge of the Golden Horn is a sentimental education about an unnamed heroine who lies about her age and signs up as a migrant worker in Germany. She works in West Berlin making radios, and lives in a women's factory hostel. The novel is not a picture of the hardships of assembly line work so much as an account of a precocious teenager refusing to become wise and a hectic four years lived between Berlin and Istanbul in a tumult of theatre, film, poetry and left-wing politics.

Emine Sevgi Özdamar was born in Turkey and attended drama school in Istanbul. She has appeared in major theatrical productions in Germany and at Vienna, Avignon and Paris, as well as in films. She has directed and written plays and her other books include the novel *Life is a Caravanserai*. She lives in Berlin.

Martin Chalmers grew up in Glasgow and now lives in Berlin. He has translated many leading German-language authors into English, including Bertolt Brecht, Erich Fried, Hans Magnus Enzensberger, Alexander Kluge, Hubert Fichte, and Elfriede Jelinek. In 2004 he was awarded the Schlegel-Tieck Translation Prize for *The Lesser Evil: The Diaries of Victor Klemperer 1945-59*.

Alkhan-Yurt

Men of the 7th climbed out of the trenches and came over to us to ask about the fight. And the infantry fluffed up their feathers and, with the casual air of seasoned soldiers, recounted their 'battle'. This was the first taste of action for many of them and it had gone well, with no casualties, and now that they had rested, they were filled with the feeling that it wasn't so terrifying; the fighting had been a piece of cake this time, and maybe it would always be that easy. They had fired and been fired at, bullets really had whistled over their heads and they'd have something to tell the folks back home. They felt like real rangers who had walked through fire and water. The adrenalin that their fear had driven out of them in huge quantities now churned in their blood, and their energy flooded back.

I looked at them with a smile and listened to their chatter – I had been like them once myself.

'... The Kombat and I were running, looking around, and this Chechen appears from a house porch to see what's happening. So the Kombat whips off his rifle and goes for him. The guy falls down and crawls round the house to croak, and the Kombat keeps firing at him, must have loosed off a whole magazine. He's got a big smirk on his face, very pleased with himself. 'Huh, dumb prick,' he says...'

'... These recon were checking out the routes to see where we could get out of the village. There weren't many of them, see, so they didn't stop to muck about, they even shot the hell out of the bushes. That's their tactic. They crawl up, hit them with a grenade launcher and pull out. When we were going to reinforce the 15th outside Oktyabrskoye they burnt out a carrier doing just that...'

'... I fell from the carrier and there were bullets going whack-whack in the branches, right over my bloody head. Man did they start up then! I crawled behind the bushes and then I saw our guys lying over in the clearing...'

No-one was paying any attention to the village now. The battle had finished, the Chechen recon we'd run into had gone, they'd either pulled out or holed up somewhere. So we relaxed. We lay on the wet ground in front of the trenches, without digging in or camouflaging ourselves, we just sat around in a group. *Which you do not do in war, under any circumstances.*

The Chechens immediately punished us for this carelessness. We all heard the whistle.

It started in the village and grew in strength, cutting through the exhaustion in our brains and throwing us onto the ground.

'Incoming!'

'Get down!'

'They aren't letting us pull back, bastards!'

We landed in the ruts. My fatigue dissolved instantly and my body was flushed with heat once again.

The first shell exploded a fair distance away from us, on the pasture. But behind this one a few more flew out of the village and exploded closer and closer as they advanced on us.

I had landed badly. I lay exposed on a slope, presenting a perfect trap for shrapnel, and I was entirely visible from all sides. The next shell hit the ground like a fat raindrop; a shower of clay clods rained down from the sky, smacking me painfully on the back of the head.

I desperately wanted to shrink, become tiny, congeal into a ball and disperse into the ground, merging with its protective lap. I even managed to picture a tiny burrow where I would be safe from shrapnel and bullets, protected from all sides as I peeped out with one eye. With every fresh explosion my desire to be in the burrow grew stronger and stronger, and with my eyes pressed tightly shut, afraid to open them before I died, I groped around in the grass for a way in.

But there was none. My body no longer responded to me; it did not want to crawl into hiding but instead became huge, filling the field, presenting a target that couldn't be missed. I would now be killed.

I shouldn't have come to Chechnya. I shouldn't have come.

Oh my God, just make it so that I'm no longer in this hellhole Chechnya, whisk me home so that the shell finds only an empty space. I swear I'll beg forgiveness from all those I wrong or failed in this life, that I'll love the whole world from now on and donate all my army wages to Chechen orphans, whatever it takes, just get me out of here. And dear God, do it right now, because here comes another.

This time it was certain death and there was nothing I could do in those rapidly contracting fragments of the only second that remained – the shell would hit much faster than I could think to race into the ditch with Igor, who had made it, faster than it took me even to move a finger – here it comes now – I leapt up with a throaty scream of defiance and fear, eyes bulging and seeing nothing but the ditch I was dashing for, slipping on the wet grass, tumbling hand and foot before I flew face down in a cowpat.

The shell dropped way beyond us and blew up on the other side of the pasture. No one moved.

Igor and I started to shift and shake off the mud. I pulled my face out of the pat, looked around through one crazed eye and mumbled, 'Got away with it.'

My head was still vacant. All I could hear ringing in my ears was the whistle of the shell, my shell, short, sharp and piercing, flying towards me again and again out of the village, coming right at me. I automatically cleaned the fresh, liquid mess from my hands, and I felt no trace of disgust; I was ready to dive straight back into shit if the need arose.

Beside us the infantry platoon commander was brushing himself off just as dismally. Standing at his full height he slowly picked off blades of grass from his trousers, one by one, and dropped them on the ground. Then he held one of them in his hand, twirled it in his fingers and said thoughtfully: 'It's actually my birthday today.'

I looked at him in silence for a few seconds, and then suddenly I began to laugh.

At first I tremored quietly, trying to contain it, but then I gave in and started to roar, louder all the time. Hysterical notes crept in, and with my head thrown back I flopped down on my knees facing the low, clouded sky, threw my arms out and howled, purging my fear with laughter, the smothering fear of a bombardment, when everything is out of your hands and you have no way of protecting yourself or saving your life, and you just lie there face down on the ground, praying that you'll get away with it this time too. It's not the rousing fear you feel in battle, but a lifeless fear, as cold as the grass you are pressing yourself into.

Igor crouched down beside me and lit up. He looked at me without saying anything for a while, then poked me in the shoulder.

'Hey, homeboy, what's with you?' Fatigue weighed heavy in his voice, making it dry and hoarse. He too had been scared, and fear ravages you, sucks the energy out of you and makes it hard even to speak.

I couldn't answer him; I carried on heaving with laughter, unable to stop. Then after I'd caught my breath, I managed to say something, punctuating my words with more chuckles.

'Birthday! Exactly! Don't worry, I'm okay, my head's still on my shoulders. You know what?' I said, wiping my tears and feeling the cow dung smear across my face. 'I just remembered. Today is the fifth of January... the fifth...

of January,' I said, still snorting.

'So what?'

'Well, it's my Olga's birthday today too, see?' I said. 'Today's the fifth of January, they've just celebrated New Year back home – belated Happy New Year to you, by the way – and now they're sitting round a table celebrating, all dressed up smart, drinking wine and eating tasty food. All they do is party and they have no idea what a bombardment is like. And people are giving my girl flowers.... They've got flowers there, imagine! Flowers! And here I am, covered in crap, with lice scuttling round my nuts, it's a scream all right!' and I burst into laughter again, falling onto my back and rolling from side to side.

The thought of flowers staggered me. I could clearly picture Olga sitting at the table covered with a white cloth, with a glass of fine white wine – she loves dry white wine and doesn't drink cheap plonk – surrounded by enormous, beautiful bouquets. She has a big smile on her face as she listens to her friends' birthday wishes for her. The room is full of bright light and the guests are wearing ties, making merry and dancing; their day's work is over and they are free of problems, they don't have to think about finding food and warmth, and instead they choose flowers for a girl. In that world there is time to work and time to have fun. And a person gets food and warmth right there in the maternity ward, along with their birth certificate.

It was only here that people got killed regardless of the time of day.

Sitting in that trench it seemed to me that there was war everywhere, that everyone was out to kill everyone else, that human grief permeated every corner of the world, right to the door of my own home, that there was no way it could be otherwise.

And yet it turns out that there is a place where people give flowers.

And that is so strange, so stupid and so funny.

Olga, Olga! What happened to our lives, what happened to the world, how did I come to be here now? Why must I now kiss a rifle instead of you, and bury my face in crap instead of in your hair? Why?

After all, these constantly drunk, unwashed contract soldiers, smeared in muck, are not the worst people in the world. We have atoned for a hundred years of sin in that marsh. So how come this is all we get for our pains? I just couldn't get my head round it all.

My darling, may everything be well with you. May you never in your life know what I've known here. May you always have a celebration, a sea of flowers, and wine and laughter. But I know that you are thinking about me now, and your face is sad. Forgive me for this. You are the brightest; you are worthy of the very best.

Let me be the one who has to die in a marsh. Lord, how we are different! Only a two-hour flight separates us, but what completely dissimilar lives we lead, we who are two identical halves! And how hard it will be to connect our lives again.

Igor took the last drag on his cigarette and ground it out. He became pensive, I could tell he was thinking of pretty dresses, perfume, wine and dancing. Then he looked at me, at my ragged jacket and filthy face, and grinned. 'Bloody right, Happy New Year.'

—

From *One Soldier's War in Chechnya* by **Arkady Babchenko**, translated from the Russian by Nick Allen (Portobello Books 2006)

Arkady Babchenko's journey from innocence to experience in the Russian Army took him from conscription at the age of 18 to a transit camp just north of Chechnya. Before he had been near the front line he learnt the meaning of violence and fear in the tradition of *dedovshchina*, the savage bullying of recruits by older soldiers (that Anna Politkovskaya also recounts in *Putin's Russia*). By the time he started active duty he was fully aware that he was fighting a war on two fronts, against the Chechen resistance and his own side.

Arkady Babchenko was drafted to fight in the first Chechen War in 1995, and then in late 1999 volunteered to return for six months during the second Chechen War. A law graduate, he currently works as a journalist on the non-conformist newspaper *Novaya Gazeta*.

Nick Allen is a British journalist working for the German Press Agency, DPA, in Pakistan. He worked in Russia for eleven years, also covering the conflict in Chechnya, and has translated for the literary journal *Glas New Russian Writing*.

The siege

What we were given to witness on the eve of the attack was more horrible than any battle, worse than any carnage. When we heard their drums roll at dusk, we first thought that, contrary to all known principles of modern war, they were perhaps about to launch a night raid. But we soon saw that what they were trying to do, once they had got their equipment ready for the assault, was to raise their soldiers' morale.

At the first beats of their drums, the sight that greeted our eyes was unbearable. Such madness we had never imagined – neither in the orgies of ancient times, whose memory has come down to us through the generations, nor in the wildest carnival nights in our own villages. Shouting, screaming, praying and dancing, men offered themselves up for sacrifice, made exhibitions of themselves in which, as we were to learn later on, severed heads carried on talking as if still in delirium; soldiers wailed as if they were night owls and banged their drums dementedly. All those noises wafted up to our castle like stinking vapours.

The light of the moon seemed to trouble and excite them at the same time. What we saw spread out beneath us was Asia in all its mysticism and barbarity, a dark grave getting ready to swallow us all.

A putrid wind was blowing up from the plain. Despite going to pray before the icon of the Virgin, our hearts sank. The cross that rises above our chapel seemed very pale, as if it had gone white with fear. But these feelings did not weaken in the slightest our determination to fight to the end. On the contrary, never before had we felt so convinced that death would be far sweeter than the gloom and treachery laid out down below in plain sight.

Our low spirits had another cause as well. There were so many of them! As many as the pebbles on a beach. And they were trying to extend their empire so the sun would never set on it, that's to say, so that night and day would be perpetually and simultaneously contained within its boundaries. They believed that when they had achieved that objective (when they had 'tied the yellow tigress and the black wolf to the same chain'), they would also rule over time itself.

That would really be the end of the world. The day God forbade, as people say in our land.

Towards midnight the hullabaloo stopped, and a deathly silence reigned.

Dawn had not quite risen when the East Tower raised the alarm. The *sentinels had noticed the gleam of torches and suspicious movements around the cannon. Our men followed instructions and left their posts to gather in the underground shelters. There we prayed with great fervour to Christ and Our Lady right up to the moment when a mortal thunder seemed to shatter heaven and earth alike. Thereupon, an infernal explosion made the ground shake beneath us. Someone yelled: 'The new weapon!' Then we heard screams, then the sound of men running who knows where.*

The war had begun.

The first attackers had now reached the top of the citadel's outer wall. Thousands of arrows spilled over their heads to protect them from the besieged. The first man grabbed the edge of the parapet. He hauled himself up on to it, then stayed still, clutching the stone to his breast, as if he had suddenly dropped off to sleep.

'They've cut off his hands,' the Quartermaster General murmured as he watched the body swoop down to the bottom again.

The second man was bent double and didn't even get to stretch out his arm. The soldier behind him clambered over his dead body with the skill of a cat and jumped over the parapet to the other side.

A Turkish fighter had at last set foot inside the fortress. Tursun Pasha closed his eyes. Don't retreat, my soldier! he implored silently.

When he opened his eyes two more fighters were on the parapet. One withdrew, and the other was thrown down, knocking another soldier off the ladder in his fall. The archers had stopped shooting now, for fear of hitting their own men. Taking advantage of the situation, dozens of defenders suddenly reappeared. Tursun Pasha thought their lances were longer than ordinary ones. In any other circumstance he would have asked what this new weapon was and where it had been forged, but his curiosity was instantly dissipated.

'At the double, send in the *eshkinxhis*!'[†] he shouted.

He watched the hindquarters of the horse bearing the herald who sped off to deliver the command.

The cheers of the *eshkinxhis* reached him in successive waves from somewhere near the right tower. At first he thought he could make out Tahanka's voice screaming above the others, but he soon realised it was only a buzzing in his own ears.

There were now dozens of ladders set against the wall, bearing more or

---

† Cavalry recruited for the campaign.

less dense bunches of men. On some of them the bodies of the dead still hung on in strange poses.

'Look at those hanging corpses,' the Quartermaster General said to the chronicler. 'The carpenters did a hasty job, and left lots of nails sticking out.'

Çelebi listened in amazement.

The forward thrust of the attackers grew more violent around the right tower. The bat-wing symbol on the crown of their helmets seemed to help them climb up. One ladder that was alive with soldiers swung back and fell into the void, but another one was put up straight away in its place.

'People who have heard Tahanka roar in battle say there is nothing more terrifying,' the Quartermaster added.

'Ah! The demons!' someone from among the Pasha's silent retinue cried out.

At that moment several bright lights flashed on the ramparts, shot out like comets, and then fell, one by one, on to the attackers.

'Fire-bombing demons!' someone muttered. Now there was a phrase that would embellish his chronicle, Çelebi thought. He said it over to himself again: fire-bombing demons. He mustn't forget it.

The crowd at the foot of the wall swayed like a stormy sea each time one of these comets shot out from behind the parapet.

'They're balls of rags soaked in a mixture of resin, sulphur, wax and oil,' the Quartermaster General explained to the chronicler. 'They make burns that never heal up entirely.'

The chronicler knew that, just as he knew many other things he pretended not to know, so as not to deprive his distinguished friend of the pleasure of explaining them to him.

'Never ever heal,' he repeated with a deep frown.

The Quartermaster General pulled up his wide sleeve to show his bare left forearm. Çelebi could barely mask a grimace.

Some of the ladders now seemed deserted. Attackers carried on storming up the others, holding their shields over their heads for protection. Down below, men ran to take shelter beneath the testudos while waiting their turn to go to the wall. Some fighting had broken out on the top of the rampart. Two of the long ladders had caught fire in several places. Another one split in two down the middle. But the number of ladders increased by the minute.

A herald galloped up.

'Burxhuba has been killed!' he yelled from a distance.

Nobody said anything.

Cannon-balls fired by the mortars constantly whistled over the defenders' heads. They were still falling inside the citadel, but the fateful moment was not far off when they would start to fall on the wall itself.

'If Saruxha manages a direct strike on the parapet, then he's a genius,' the Quartermaster General said. 'But he's being cautious, and quite right too. Just a few paces off target, and our own men will be pulp.'

A cannon-ball then hit the parapet dead on. The bunch of defenders preparing to repel a new wave of attackers was annihilated. Dismembered body parts rained down together with lumps of masonry.

'Bravo!' someone standing behind the Pasha cried out.

The almost entirely demolished parapet at the spot where the mortar had struck stayed empty for a moment or two. The *azabs*‡ rushed into the breach and were quickly in command of the rampart walk. One of them unfurled a standard. Cheers rose from all around, in a deep-throated clamour. The flag fluttered for a moment, but then something happened: long black lances emerged from all around the men, a struggle ensued, and then the flag disappeared as if it had been whisked away by a gust of wind.

Meanwhile, to the left of the main gate, a horde of attackers thrust forwards towards the great breach. Some climbed along on wide ladders, others were moving screens towards the places where molten pitch and fireballs were hitting the ground. Many *azabs* had caught fire and were running away with their arms flailing, looking like giant torches. Some of them rolled themselves on the ground to put out the flames that were consuming them. Others pranced about like lunatics among the throng which parted in terror to leave them passage, then crawled along the ground, got up, fell again, and finally groaned until their last breath. Smoke still rose from the dead as if their souls were not finding it easy to quit the body.

Çelebi had been wondering for a while about how to find an image that would properly translate the sight of these burning men. He thought of comparing them to moths fluttering round a cresset, but the word 'moth' hardly seemed adequate to suggest the ardour and heroism of these fighters. However nothing else occurred to him, and, in addition, if he likened the fires of a holy war to the candle of Islam, as he had read in ancient chronicles, then the word 'moth' might do in the end. He could call these soldiers 'the moths of the Sacred Candle'.

Suddenly the earth shook and a terrific clap of thunder cut off the train

‡ Infantry units.

of his thoughts. The Pasha and his retinue turned towards where the noise had come from. Something had happened somewhere near the artillery. A great column of black smoke rose into the sky in that quarter. An officer rushed off at a gallop.

Everyone behind the Pasha started asking questions in muffled tones. A few moments later the officer came back.

'One of the mortars has exploded,' he reported. 'Many men killed, and many others wounded.'

'And the master caster?' the Pasha asked.

'He is unharmed.'

The Pasha turned back towards the citadel and nobody dared say another word.

He ordered fresh troops to move up to the assault. As he watched the Persian and Caucasian regiments dashing towards the walls to relieve the *azabs* and the *eshkinxhis* (as for the volunteers, they were for the most part no such thing), the commander-in-chief thought to himself that it was still too soon to send in the elite units of the *dalkiliç* *, which he usually threw into battle after the janissaries.

The assault was now in progress along the entire length of the citadel's surrounding wall. There were hundreds of ladders large and small reaching up to the parapets or to the edges of the breaches opened in the masonry. They sucked up a proportion of the flood of soldiers swirling at their feet and raised them to the top of the wall. And as soon as those scorched and bloodied men clambered over the parapet or through the breach, they threw away their shields so as to brandish their adzes and swords. The shields, dripping with pitch and molten wax, fell on top of the soldiers following behind, and they screamed as they tried to avoid being hit by the falling objects.

'They've not stopped climbing,' the Quartermaster General said pensively. His tone seemed to say: they are climbing, but what's the use? 'It seems to me we are fighting a losing battle,' he added in a dull voice.

'A losing battle,' the chronicler repeated to himself. The words were so terrible as to stick in your throat.

The *eshkinxhis* pressed on obstinately up the escarpment.

* Swordsmen

From *The Siege* by **Ismail Kadare**, translated from the French of Jusuf Vrioni by David Bellos (Canongate Books 2008)

The Siege is Ismail Kadare's account of Albania's confrontation with the Ottoman Empire, a portrait of war that resonates from the early fifteenth century to the most recent Balkan wars at the end of the twentieth. Sparely written, as if a myth or a legend, and lit with scrupulous detail, it confirms Kadare as one of Europe's most significant novelists.

Ismail Kadare was born in 1936 in Gjirokastër, southern Albania, and his novels have been translated in more than forty countries. His first novel to appear in English was *A Chronicle in Stone* in 1987. In 1996 he became a member of the French Academy of Moral and Political Sciences and in 2005 he was awarded the first Man Booker International Prize for 'a body of work written by an author who has had a truly global impact'.

David Bellos, Director of the Program in Translation at Princeton University, is the translator of Georges Perec's *Life: A User's Manual* and a winner of the Goncourt Prize for Poetry. He has translated seven of Ismail Kadare's novels, and in 2005 was awarded the Translator's Man Booker International Prize for his translations of Kadare's work.

(The sin is not to love)

An unfortunate coincidence. I'm not sure what to call it. Faustino Manso, my father, died yesterday evening. Disembarking at the airport I bought a copy of the *Jornal de Angola*. The story – short, dry – appeared on the culture page:

'Wandering Mousebird dies – Faustino Manso died early yesterday morning, at the Sacred Hope Clinic on Luanda Island, after a long illness. He was eighty-one. Manso, known to his admirers as The Wandering Mousebird, was a popular musician through the 1960s and seventies, not only in Angola but throughout southern Africa. He had lived in a number of Angolan cities, as well as in Cape Town in South Africa, and Maputo (then still called Lourenço Marques). He returned to Luanda, his birthplace, in 1975, immediately after independence. For many years he worked for the National Institute for Books and Records. He leaves a widow – Senhora Anacleta Correia da Silva Manso – and three children and twelve grandchildren.'

I find the obituary pages more eloquent. There are four announcements bearing the name Faustino Manso. One is signed by Anacleta Correia da Silva Manso – this is the longest. The photo, too, is slightly larger, and more recent. Its words, thus:

'You left without a final farewell, my husband, and the sun in my life has gone out. The magnificent voice has fallen silent: who now will sing to me as I do my embroidery? You deceived me, you promised me that you'd stay with me till I reached the end, that you'd take my hand so I wouldn't be afraid. But I feel afraid now. As it turned out you did leave me again, for such a long journey – I don't know whether I will be able to forgive you.'

The second is signed by his three children: N'Gola, Francisca (Cuca) and João (Johnny). The photograph shows Faustino Manso with a guitar in his arms.

'Dear father, we met you very late, but, fortunately, not too late. You have left us, but you have left us your songs. We sing with you today: *No roads have an end / too far from your embrace.*'

The third and fourth announcements took me by surprise. I sat down – shaken – on my suitcase. I asked Mandume to go buy me a bottle of water. It was only then that I noticed the heat, I think. It rose from the floor, thick and humid, stuck itself to your skin, entangled itself in your hair, acidic as the breath of an old man. Someone by the name of Fatita de Matos, of Benguela, had put her name to the only announcement that didn't carry a photograph; her words were brief, but explicit:

'The sin is not to love. A greater sin is not to love until the very end of love. I don't regret any of it, Tino, my Mousebird. Rest in peace.'

In the final announcement, my father appears posing for posterity, vigorous in his thirties, sitting at a table in a bar. He has a bottle of beer in front of him. It is possible to make out the label: Cuca. As I write these notes I'm drinking a Cuca too. It is good – very light, fresh. I read the words again:

'Dear father, hug our mother when you find her – Leopoldina has waited so long for that hug. Tell her that her children – your children – miss her terribly; we think of you every day, we are guided by the example of your courage and honesty, and will always be guided by it. Our world has become sadder without the joy of your double bass in it. Who will play it now? Your children: Babaera and Smirnoff.'

Mandume's parents had got married in Lisbon, in 1975; they were both twenty years old. Marcolino studied architecture. Manuela, nursing. They must have been quite naïve, still are even today. Manuela said to me:

'At that time we were all nationalists, it was like a sickness. We hated Portugal. We wanted to finish our courses and return to the trenches of socialism in Africa.'

Manuela gave me old records to listen to, vinyl, of Angolan music. There are various songs that refer to the trenches of socialism in Africa. Just like that, without the slightest shadow of irony. Portuguese bureaucracy wouldn't accept that the couple's first son should be called Mutu, in tribute to a king from Angola's central plateau: Mutu-ya-Kevela. So for official purposes he was Marcelo, and Mutu to family and close friends. Mandume, the middle son, is actually called Mariano, and Mandela, the youngest, Martinho. In 1977, the year Mandume was born, Marcolino's two brothers were shot in Luanda, accused of involvement in an attempted *coup d'état*. Marcolino was very upset. He never again spoke of going back. Once his course was finished he found himself a job in the studio of an architect – himself also an Angolan – applied for Portuguese nationality and dedicated himself completely to his work. I met Mandume seven months ago. The first thing that attracted me to him was his eyes. The shine in his eyes. His hair, divided into little spiky locks, gives him the look of a rebel, in contrast with the sweetness of his gestures and his voice. I like to watch him walking. The world he moves in has no friction.

'Like a cat?'

Aline, in a whisper, her lips moist, leaning over the table. 'When we say someone moves smoothly, it makes people think of cats.' No, dear Aline,

Mandume is not like a cat. There's something about the way cats move, a kind of arrogance, an imperial disdain for poor humanity, and that's nothing like Mandume. He is simultaneously humble and defiant. At least, that's how he looks to me. Maybe that's just through my eyes. Maybe it's love. Aline laughed, and I remember her laughing the first time I talked to her about Mandume. She has a lovely laugh. She is my best friend.

'And Mandume, what does it mean?'

Mandume? Ah, another king. A Cuanhama tribal chief who killed himself during a battle, in the south of Angola, against German troops. Mandume – my Mandume – isn't very interested in finding out about the historical figure who gave him his name. When I asked him what he was called he said:

'Mariano. Mariano Maciel.'

And it was Mário, a sound technician, a short, pale man with very fair hair, thinning but long, who interjected, smiling:

'So, Mandume, the whitest black man in Portugal.'

An unfortunate thing to say. I reacted violently.

'Oh yes?! Is that supposed to be a compliment?'

It was supposed to be a compliment. Today I'm tempted to agree with poor Mário, and I've even used the same phrase to Mandume myself. There are moments when I feel truly in love with him. Others, however, when I practically hate him. I get irritated by the contempt he demonstrates towards Africa. Mandume decided to be Portuguese. He does have the right. However I don't think that in order to be a good Portuguese person you have to renounce your entire ancestry. I'm sure I'm a good Portuguese woman, but I also feel a little bit Indian; and now at last I've come to Angola to find out whether there's anything in me that's African.

Mandume came with me, reluctantly.

'Have you gone mad? What are you going to do in Africa?'

Finally he came in order to save me from Africa. He came in order to save us. He's a sweetheart, I know, I should be more patient with him. Besides which, he enjoys what he's doing. He spends the day following me around with the video camera. I tell him to film that or this, which he pretends to do, but when I realise what's going on, he's filming me.

From *My Father's Wives* by **José Eduardo Agualusa**, translated from the Portuguese by Daniel Hahn (Arcadia Books 2008)

My Father's Wives is the story of Laurentina's journey from her home in Portugal to Angola to trace the story of the father she never knew, celebrated Angolan musician Faustino Manso. But José Eduardo Agualusa's fiction runs in parallel with his story of the novel's genesis, as writer and characters travel the southern African coast, from Angola through Namibia and South Africa to Mozambique, uncovering Faustino's secrets along the way.

José Eduardo Agualusa is one of the leading literary voices from Angola, and from the Portuguese language today. His *The Book of Chameleons* won the 2007 Independent Foreign Fiction Prize. Agualusa divides his time between Angola, Brazil and Portugal.

Daniel Hahn is a writer of non-fiction, the editor of reference books for adults and children, and a translator. His translations include Agualusa's novels *Creole*, *The Book of Chameleons*, *My Father's Wives* and *Rainy Season*, and the autobiography of Brazilian footballer Pelé.

Third defeat: 1941 or
the language of the dead

The next day was Sunday. All the prisoners were forced to attend mass, which the chaplain said inside their cell. In his fierce, patriotic homily he talked about the Babe. With all the fury of an archangel, he condemned his suicide, but did not mention any other deaths. The prisoners listened in absolute silence. Those of them with a more highly-developed survival instinct went up to receive Communion. One of them was the boy with nits. When they returned to their places, the communicants covered their faces with their hands, more to hide their feelings of shame than out of any religious conviction.

When Juan asked the boy if he thought that by taking Communion he could change his destiny, the lad said perhaps, but that anyway the wafer was something to eat, and he was always starving.

The chaplain's sermon led Juan to finish his letter as quickly as possible. There was something in the nature of time passing so slowly which seemed to precipitate and accelerate events, even though every second dragged by with such exasperating slowness.

As soon as Juan was able to get away from the others, he took out the paper and pencil again and went on writing:

... I'm still alive. The language of my dreams is increasingly accessible to me. When I want to show affection I talk about amortesy, and gentlety is the rare quality possessed by those who are kind to me. Hillain, cliffside, dreamscape, highcave, are words people in my dreams use to tell me about yearned-for landscapes and places beyond our barriers. They call anything that makes a drumming sound heartchimes, and wolf-flint is the howling of the wind. They call the sound of water in streams roargurgle. I love speaking their language.

The lad with nits came and sat by him. He said nothing. Juan broke off his letter, and realised he had learned to catalogue sadness, to distinguish between all the different kinds of despair, to recognise fear mixed with hate, hatred on its own, and fear in its pure state. He even knew how to spot the difference between someone who was sorry for not doing something from someone who was sorry for having done something. But the boy beside him had a gaping hole deep in his eyes that came from something Juan had almost forgotten: a sense of loss. That was probably why the two of them began to talk in a leisurely way, gazing out at the sky beyond the bars of the window. Juan told him about Mozart – another of the defeated, and about Salieri. He talked about the scientist Ramón y Cajal – another solitary fighter – and of how clouds are formed. He went on to mention Darwin and how important the thumb was for man to become man, how it helped him climb down from trees and learn to kill his fellows.

'But everything that took place, the Popular Front, the war, was to put an end to all that, wasn't it?'

That freezing afternoon in a cell ineluctably disconnected from the natural flow of life, Juan did not have the strength to console him. All the effort had been useless because the starting point was wrong. Whatever you do, half the people are going to be against you. It's a punishment. So nobody is obliged to get it right. Am I boring you?

'What I wouldn't give to be able to roll a cigarette!' was the boy's only reply.

Talking like this they somehow forgot death. Sunday passed by furtively in a city steeped in fear. After that came day after day of dawn lists and orders to appear before Colonel Eymar's tribunal. But as time went on, there were more days of rest as well. One day there were no death trucks, the next no one had to appear before the Tribunal of Repression of Masons and Communism... and Juan was never summoned.

A few weeks later, as night was falling, he heard his name shouted out again in the corridor, and once again Sergeant Edelmiro escorted him to the dark room next to the kitchens. Inside were the fierce, hapless colonel and his wife, wrapped as ever in her astrakhan coat. As soon as she saw Juan, she handed him a jersey that had once been green. 'It belonged to Miguelito,' she told him, then launched into fresh questions as if their previous conversation had taken place just the day before.

She told him stories about her son. Juan responded with more lies: he remembered that once Miguel had taken off his own woollen socks to lend to a prisoner who was shivering with cold, or another occasion when he had thrown his meal in the face of a cook who had refused to give any bread to a prisoner who sang the nationalist anthem whenever anyone barked orders at him...

These stories were not entirely invented, but they were attributed to someone who did not deserve to be their protagonist. Miguel Eymar was not a person about whom anything heroic, or even defiant, could be said. The strategy worked, as Juan Senra could tell when twice Sergeant Edelmiro was ignored as he poked his head round the door and uttered a servile 'At your orders, colonel sir', and at the end when Colonel Eymar's impatience spilled over in a gentle 'Please, Violeta, it's late' or 'Violeta, we only have permission for fifteen minutes', and she opened her bag and offered him a herring roll wrapped in brown paper.

'I'll be back,' she said defiantly, staring straight at her husband.

Juan put up with Eduardo López's routine questioning, and shared the roll with the boy with nits. What made the political commissar think that some day he might be able to use all the information he was collecting? The fact that he was still alive was nothing more than mere chance, one of death's arbitrary decisions. Besides, they had no contact whatsoever with the world outside – and yet there he was, the disciplined party man, accumulating information and analysing the prisoners' behaviour.

Juan put a stop to their conversation with vague replies. Life smelled of herrings, and nothing could be more marvellous.

The days rolled by. March was cold and damp, as befits unlived time. Even though he found it hard to wear Miguel Eymar's jersey, Juan was glad of the warmth it gave him through the endless nights.

The dawn lists continued, but were shorter each time. What was more encouraging still, they learned of several prisoners who had been given life sentences rather than shot.

That was almost like being alive.

Juan had another visit from the woman in the astrakhan coat and her henpecked husband. He lied once more, inventing heroic stories and events that brought a smile to pale, stiff lips nobody could ever imagine were capable of kissing. As with Sherezade, his lies bought him another night of life. And another.

And another.

Until one day when the first name on the list to appear before Colonel Eymar was the lad with nits. Juan waited the entire day for the prisoners to return. He pushed past the others to the window and shouted if anyone knew what had happened to Eugenio Paz. Nobody had any idea. That was the start of several days of an anguish that was new to Juan, like anguish piled on anguish, uncertainty added to uncertainty.

The larva-like existence in prison so quickly generates a catalogue of emotions, of memories crammed into this narrow period of time, that prisoners are amazed that to create their earlier emotions, those beyond the prison walls, they needed an entire, intensely-lived life. In spite of this, Juan was horrified to think that, if we were alive in our tombs, we would probably end up loving the worms.

He used Miguel Eymar's jersey to bribe Sergeant Edelmiro, but learned only that Paz was on the fourth floor, not what his sentence had been. He tried to send him a message, but had nothing left to pay for any favours. So Eugenio Paz never found out that Juan Senra had embraced him as a friend and brother.

He never knew that Juan Senra was asking where he could find the pregnant girl from Seville to tell her Eugenio was faithful and missed her so much. He never knew that Juan was worried about the way he rubbed his head raw when he tried to scratch the lice.

Then one morning, peering up at the bars of the glassless window, he heard Eugenio Paz's name called out by the officer who read the list of those condemned to die that day. Juan made the last physical effort of his life and pulled himself up level with the window. He shouted at the top of his voice:

'Eugenio! Don't get on the lorry! It's me, Juan!'

The officer's voice went on reading out names, as though nothing and nobody could stop him. Gradually, Juan's hands slipped from the bars and he fell in a heap on the floor. He cried in a way he no longer thought possible after living through a war. As the noise of the lorry died away outside the prison gate, an interpreter of tears, some expert translator of sobs, might have caught the fact that, in the midst of all his gasping lament, Juan had said the word 'Farewell'. But nobody did hear him, and for two days and nights he was gripped by a lethargy that was impervious to cold and hunger as well as to any encouragement. It was as though his biology had ceased to function, as if time itself had died of sadness.

Juan knew he did not have long to finish his letter. He wrote in a neat, tiny handwriting until he had filled all the paper he had managed to obtain:

I'm still alive, but by the time you receive this letter I'll have been shot. I've tried to go mad but cannot. I refuse to go on living with all this sadness. I've discovered that the language I dreamt in order to create a happier world is in fact the language of the dead. Remember me always and try to be happy. Your loving brother, Juan.

He tried to imagine how the chaplain would react when he came to censor the letter. He licked the envelope, wrote his brother's address on the front, and handed it to the guard on duty. This was what they always did.

This was how the dead always said goodbye to the living.

On the third day, Sergeant Edelmiro repeated his name until Juan finally stirred out of his stupor. Someone helped him to the cell door. This time the two soldiers did not walk flanking him: they needed all their strength to carry him to the room where the woman in the astrakhan coat was waiting. There she was, concerned and maternal, a dark vampire concealing the slight figure of Colonel Eymar, who as always hovered in the background.

She asked if he was ill. It took Juan a long time to reply, as though he had not understood. When he finally did, it was to say: 'I'm dead.' 'Oh come on, come on,' she said, trying to encourage him. She led him over to the ledge. It will all be over one day. Juan let her lead him to sit down, but shook his head.

'You're young. All this will be over one day. You'll see.' Juan was still shaking his head softly. 'I've brought you a roll.'

'I'm not hungry.'

'You need to eat, you don't look well.'

'I'm fine.'

'So what's wrong?'

Juan took a good look at these two sickly-sweet beings who were talking and behaving as if they owned him. Juan was their plaything, something that was meant to perform once they had wound him up, to move when they gave him a push, to stop when told to do so. That was why they could not understand his behaviour now.

'The thing is, I've remembered,' he said.

The woman in astrakhan made the mistake of asking him what he had remembered that made him feel so ill.

Juan told her he had remembered the truth. That her son had been justifiably shot because he was a criminal, and not a war criminal, where guilt or innocence depended on which side was doing the judging, but a common criminal, a thief, someone who murdered civilians to steal from them and sell what did not belong to him on the black market, a gang leader who had not even shown loyalty to his fellows. Thanks to him, they had rounded up a whole organisation of traitors, thanks to his tip-off they had broken up a network that dealt in contaminated medicines. Fortunately not even being a coward had worked in his favour, because in the end he had been given a fair trial, condemned to death, and shot even more fairly by a firing squad. And he did not die a hero's death. I – in this Juan Senra was lying – I was in charge of the squad that executed him. He shit himself, he cried, he begged us not to kill him, he promised he would tell us more about the organisations loyal to Franco still hiding in Madrid... he was scum, and died like scum. Everything I told you before was lies. I did it so that I could live, but I no longer want to live if it means I have to give you comfort. Now I want to go.

All this was like a thunderbolt, an earth tremor that took Colonel Eymar and his wife's breath away. They listened in silence to this rapid sketch of their son, done in colours they knew at once were the colours of truth. Nobody lies when they want to die.

They did not even protest when Juan Senra walked out of the room he had been carried into, or when he ordered the sergeant outside to take him back to his cell, even though the soldier looked to the colonel for confirmation. He interpreted the glassy look in the officer's eyes as approval, and, feeling obliged to look more professional, straightened up and roughly pushed Juan Senra along the corridor in front of him. He kept a safe distance behind his prisoner as they climbed the stairs back up to the second floor.

Juan said nothing to anyone. He did not queue with his bowl for the evening broth, but stood silently beneath the window, imagining a vast grey sky beyond its bars that had the power to abolish all sign of spring.

Two days later, his name was first on the list of those summoned before the tribunal. He was the first to appear before Colonel Eymar. He was the first person condemned to death that day. None of the threats from Lieutenant Rioboo or any of the blows in the face from the albino, flag-doodling clerk could force him to stand to attention.

At first light the next morning, his was the first name on the list of those taken out into the yard. As the lorry carrying him and the other condemned men to La Almudena cemetery emerged from the prison gate, Juan Senra thought Eduardo López would be relieved now there was no longer any reason to keep him alive. He tried to guess what arcane criteria the chaplain had used to censor the letter he had written his brother. It reassured him to think it would never be sent.

He also thought – and this too gave him a certain satisfaction – that the smug look of triumph must have disappeared forever from Colonel Eymar's face.

He only stopped hating when he thought of his brother.

From *Blind Sunflowers* by **Alberto Méndez**, translated from the Spanish by Nick Caistor (Arcadia Books 2008)

These are stories from silent times, when people feared that others might discover what they knew, when the victorious and defeated of the Spanish Civil War lost or feared losing their sense of direction, like blind sunflowers. Whatever a person's affiliation, nobody survived the war, or Franco's peace that replaced it, unscathed.

    Alberto Méndez worked for both Spanish and international publishing companies before writing *Blind Sunflowers*, which was awarded the 2004 Sentenil Prize and the 2005 National Prize for Literature. Méndez died in 2004.

Nick Caistor is a British writer who has translated more than thirty books from the Spanish, including works by Juan Carlos Onetti, Juan Marsé and Eduardo Mendoza. In 2007 he was awarded the Valle-Inclan Translation Prize for his version of *The Sleeping Voice* by Dulce Chacón.

Clothes

The auditorium in the village cultural centre is open once a week, on Thursdays. Anyone can come in and take a look, so people come from the local area but from far away as well. They believe that this is where they will discover the truth. There is a stage in the auditorium but no seating for an audience. The clothes are laid out on the terracotta floor. They've already been sorted: this was found on the first person, that on the seventieth. Everything has been laundered to restore its colour, then hung on a line to dry. The coloured items of clothing are now lying close together side by side, though each one is by itself. There is rarely a complete outfit. For example, right by the entrance there is just a blue-and-white-striped T-shirt. It must have been worn by a well-built man, whereas someone skinny must have gone around in the one with 'Montana' written on it. Further on there are some corduroy trousers, once white, now yellow. Who wore them? Under the window there's a single jeans leg. Whose? Further on there's just a leather belt, just a pair of briefs, just one gym shoe, a single black sock. Next to each set of clothes (or rather rags) sits the empty paper bag they've been taken out of, and a sheet of paper with a large number, printed on a computer.

There are letters too:

B – That means the clothes have a matching set of bones, a skull and teeth. There is an entire *B*ody.
BP – There is no complete set, but there are some bones. *B*ody *P*arts.
A – Clothing only, maybe some objects (*A*rtefacts). No bones.

All of this was dug up in the autumn of 1999 in nearby Kevljani (thus before each number we also have the letters KV). The mass grave there was a long one, stretching several hundred metres along the road (the roadside ditch was made deep enough in advance, and filled in afterwards). Kevljani is near the town of Omarska, where in 1992 a concentration camp for Muslims was set up in a mine and completed its business that same year. Almost all the prisoners were men, though there were some women, most of whom survived.

The relatives of missing persons who have reasons to believe they ended up in Omarska eight years ago report to the auditorium. They come in and hold their noses, but they have no alternative; they cannot give up. They have come here to see, find and bury. They believe that afterwards they will feel relief and find peace.

They look around. Between one set of clothing and another there is a narrow aisle. To avoid disturbing anything with their shoes, they walk as if along a line. They bend over something. No-one is sure; each of them moves on, stops, then moves on again. This goes on for half an hour, an hour or three hours, as each person wishes.

There are rats running around in the hall.

A young couple carrying a seven-year-old girl are looking for their father, the little girl's grandfather. For a long while they stand over clothing KV22B.

A grey-haired lady in a navy-blue suit is bending over some other ragged pieces of clothing. She has been bending over the same outfit since morning. She keeps arranging it, as if she wanted it to look presentable. She straightens out the dark trousers, light shirt and something that used to be a dark-red sweater. She caresses it all just as you would caress a person.

She is known as Mother Mejra.

The young people with the seven-year-old girl who have spent such a long time near the stage looking at clothing KV22B call over the person in charge of identification. She is an energetic white-haired woman in jeans. Her name is Ewa Elwira Klonowski.

Dr Ewa Klonowski was born in 1946. By training an anthropologist, a member of the American Academy of Forensic Sciences, she is a wife and mother who emigrated from Poland during martial law. She used to live in Wroclaw but now lives permanently in Reykjavik in Iceland. There she became a specialist in paternity inquiries, because she could not work in the field that fascinates her the most: bones.

'I love bones; bones speak to me. I can look at some bones and I know what illnesses the person had, how he walked, how he liked to sit. I can determine nationality by bones. A Muslim's femur is bent into a slight arc, because Muslims squat. Japanese have the same feature because they often kneel.'

History has given Dr Klonowski the chance to do some fascinating work in Bosnia and Herzegovina. The war and the end of the war have meant concentration camps, mass executions, mass graves, mass exhumations and the need for identification.

Dr Klonowski had herself inoculated against tetanus and jaundice and packed her bags. Her husband and two teenage daughters saw her off at the airport.

She has been working in Bosnia since 1996, first for the International Tribunal at The Hague (the judges want to know who did the killing, how they did it and how many people were killed; they do not need to know the victims' names). Now, for Icelandic and American government money, she works for the Bosnian Commission on Missing Persons (for whom identification of the victims is the priority). Dr Klonowski has dug up some two thousand bodies. She has fished them out of wells, extracted them from caves, and dug them out of rubbish dumps or from under piles of pig bones.

Now she is checking something in her papers, putting on her rubber gloves and going up onto the stage. The young woman and her husband (who is still carrying their daughter) are standing in front of it. Dr Klonowski steps (cautiously, to avoid treading on anything) among some small, tightly sealed plastic bags. She is looking for the one with the number KV22B.

She has found the right bag now, and opens it. She takes out an upper jawbone, a lower one with several teeth in it, and some loose teeth. She fits them into the right sockets and deftly assembles the entire jaw. She goes up to the edge of the stage and shows it to the family.

'Could this be your father?' she asks.

The young woman examines the jaw closely, and looks at her husband as if he might give her some advice. Their little daughter is holding her nose.

'Yes, that could be my father,' says the woman quite calmly.

'Okay,' says Dr Klonowski, packing the jaw back into the bag and returning it to its place. 'Let's move on.'

'On' means to the other end of the village (which is called Lu˘sci Palanka), where there is a concrete barracks, once a workers' canteen.

A few months ago some large tables were set up in front of the barracks, and a hosepipe was brought over from the nearest farm. The locals gathered around the tables – men, women and children. They watched as Dr Klonowski sorted out the bones, determining gender and age, and packed them into body bags.

Now the body bags are lying on the ground in the dark barracks, waiting for someone to claim them. They are white plastic bags with zip fasteners – a bit like protective covers for men's suits but two metres long.

We look for body bag KV22B. There it is, lying against the wall, right in the corner, under some others. Dr Klonowski sets the ones lying on top to one side and pulls out the right one. She undoes the zip. The little girl watches; no-one moves a muscle. Dr Klonowski is not surprised. She was surprised when she first started working in Bosnia four years ago.

'Why do you drag your children here?' she had asked.

'So they will remember.' Everyone gave the same reply.

'Did your father have a problem with his hip?' asks the doctor, holding one part of a hip joint in her right hand, another in her left.

'Yes, he did have some trouble,' says the young woman. 'He had an operation.'

'But did he walk like this?' asks the doctor, imitating someone waddling.

'No, I don't think so.'

'This one definitely walked like that. You must find the hospital where your father had his operation. They might have some documents.'

'All right. I'll come next Thursday.'

'Then we'll take some blood from you. We'll compare your DNA with DNA from these bones. We'll be a hundred per cent sure.'

Now Dr Klonowski has time for a break. We go back to the cultural centre.

The grey-haired lady in the navy-blue suit whom we saw earlier leaves her preferred clothing unattended for a while. In the room next door she makes us some coffee.

'I am Mother Mejra.' She introduces herself. 'I come here every Thursday. I help Dr Ewa, and I comfort the families.'

Mejra Dautović, aged fifty-eight, used to live in Prijedor. That spring, the Serbs had herded the young Muslim men along the streets in front of them as a human shield to protect them from the local territorial defence force. Serbian flags were flown from the official buildings and stations. The Muslims were ordered to hang white sheets out of their windows, and to wear white armbands. Snipers took up positions in the housing blocks.

Nowadays Prijedor is in the Serb Republic. There is no place there for Mother Mejra. She and her husband now live in Bosanski Petrovac, in a house that is Serbian, not their own.

We follow Mejra along the narrow aisles between the scraps of clothing. We stand over that set of clothes – the dark trousers, light shirt and something that used to be a dark-red sweater. Mother Mejra leans over to straighten a trouser leg. She stands up and tries to decide if it all looks reasonably presentable.

'This is Edvin,' she says, as if introducing someone to us. 'My son. The sex matches, and the age, and the height, and the teeth. But Dr Ewa isn't completely sure. They haven't done our DNA tests yet. I had Edvin' – she leans over to adjust the trouser leg again – 'and I had Edna. I know all about what happened to my Edna. Who beat her up, who raped her. The only thing I don't know is where that bus went. Where they took her from Omarska. Her clothes are nowhere to be found, not even a shoe, nothing.'

For several years Mother Mejra has been travelling around the area, putting photographs of her children up on walls. She has even written a book about them. She is intent on finding any information at all that will lead her to the truth. She wants to find out three things: How did her children die? Who killed them? Where are their bones?

From *Like Eating a Stone* by **Wojciech Tochman**, translated from the Polish by Antonia Lloyd Jones *(Portobello Books 2009)*

During four years of war in Bosnia more than 100,000 people lost their lives, but it was months, even years, before the mass graves started to yield their dead and the process of identification, burial and mourning could begin. Wojciech Tochman travelled through the post-war landscape in the company of a few of those who survived, as they visited the scenes of their loss. His book is both a series of snapshots and of memorials to those who were afforded respect neither in life nor in death, until their families were able to look for them again.

Wojciech Tochman is an award-winning Polish reporter and writer. *Like Eating A Stone* was shortlisted for the NIKE Polish Literary Prize and for the Prix Témoin du Monde, awarded by Radio France International.

Antonia Lloyd Jones' translations from Polish include works by Joanna Olczak-Ronikier, Jaroslaw Iwaszkiewicz, and Pawel Huelle, whose novels *Who was David Weiser?* and *Mercedes-Benz* were both shortlisted for the Independent Foreign Fiction Prize.

Out of three hundred and thirty Sarajevo numbers rung at random, about every fifteenth has an answering machine

Good evening, my name is Aleksandar Krsmanović. I'm calling you because I'm trying to find out something about a childhood friend. She escaped from Višegrad to Sarajevo during the civil war. Her name is Asija. I've tried everything I can, the civil service offices, the Internet – no luck. I can't tell you her surname because unfortunately I'm not sure if I've got it right. If you know anything about anyone of that name, please call me on 00 49 1748 526368. Asija is in her early twenties now, and back then she had extremely bright blonde hair. Thank you very much.

Good evening, my name is Aleksandar Krsmanović. I'm calling you because I'm trying to find out something about a childhood friend. She escaped from Višegrad to Sarajevo during the civil war. Her name is Asija. I've tried everything else, the civil service offices, the Internet – no luck. I can't tell you her surname because unfortunately I'm not sure if I've got it right. If you know anything about anyone of that name, please call me on 00 49 1748 526368. Asija is in her early twenties now, and back then she had extremely bright blonde hair. Thank you very much.

Hello? Mr Sutijan? I hope I'm pronouncing your name correctly – I called your number at random because I'm so disappointed by my efforts to date. My name is Aleksandar and I'm calling from Germany, where I've been living since our war. Do you happen to know a woman called Asija? It's not a common name, maybe you've heard it and could give me a clue where to find her. The name means bringer of peace, I'm looking for my own Asija and I can't be at peace until I know what's happened to her. That may sound naff and drunk, and so it is too. Mr Sutijan, if anything occurs to you, my number is: 00 49 1748 526368.

Hello, Asija, this is Aleksandar. You're not there. I've just booked a flight to Sarajevo. I'm arriving on Monday. I'd like it if we could meet. You can reach me on: 00 49 1748 526368.

Hello, this is Aleksandar Krsmanović. Asija? It would be nice if we could meet, I'm arriving on the twenty-fifth. There won't be any ripe elderberries and plums and quinces yet, but there'll be stairwells around smelling delicious. You can call me if you like on 00 49 1748 526368.

Asija? This is Aleksandar. Aleksandar with the big ears from Višegrad. The boy in the cellar. The one who called you Beautiful because there wasn't any better word to describe the colour of your hair. Aleksandar who was your brother for a day. Let's meet in Sarajevo or Višegrad and remember what we went through together. 00 49 1748 526368.

Asija? Hi, Aleksandar here. Mondays are the best days to begin something. It's almost ten years since we last met. That makes about five hundred and twenty Mondays, which doesn't sound like much. But if you think about it carefully, it's a whole lot of Mondays when something new could have begun. I'd like to know all the things you've begun in your life. I'm going to spend a few days where I once came to the end of something. 00 49 1748 526368.

I've written six letters, Asija, and I thought up a different surname for you for each envelope, but I always wrote the same one in the end. Bosnia is boundless compared to just six letters. In my imagination I see you as a violinist. You have tough, hardened skin on your fingertips and you wear yourself out at every concert. If someone asks how you're doing, you hardly know where to begin for pride. You run five kilometres every day, you speak French, but you couldn't care less about France. I'll be in Bosnia from Monday, please call me: 00 49 1748 526368.

Good evening, this is Aleksandar. Asija…? Are you there…? Please pick up the phone… I miss you, you see, and if you pick up the phone maybe I can tell you what exactly it is I miss about you. Things build up over ten years. How do you do your hair now? Do you like minced meat? I love minced meat. I'll be in Sarajevo on Monday, for three days. 00 49 1748 526368.

I'm sorry to trouble you. Once upon a time there was a blonde girl with the Arabic name of Asija and a dark-haired boy with the far from Arabic name of Aleksandar. There was a definite chance of a love story there: their parents might have come over all religious and opposed the connection, convention opposes it anyway, and war makes all those objections even stronger. Terrible, because the heart has its reasons and so on and so forth. I have to disappoint you. Asija and Aleksandar were too young for a love story. They didn't yet have any sense of the tragic potential of their happiness and possible unhappiness. Asija who was protected! Aleksandar who protected her! Ha! The two of them held hands and switched the light on at a time when only lunatics thought of being light-hearted. 00 49 1748 526368. That's my number, in case you'd like to know more. Sorry to trouble you.

My cases are packed. The wine tastes good. The plums that grow in Višegrad are better than any others. 00 49 1748 526368. You can reach me at any time, any time over the last ten years, so to speak. I'm writing a portrait of Višegrad in thirty lists. But first I'm coming to see you, Asija.

Hello, good evening. I'm nothing special. My story is nothing special. Good evening. I arrive too late for everything. I arrive too late to be special. I'm arriving at the story of my life too late. Good evening, Bosnia, please call back: 00 49 1748 526368.

Asija, I'll look for your hair, I'll look on all the faces I see for your forehead. I'll drop your name into every conversation like a seed and hope it will grow into a flower. Dear answering machine, do you know a flower called Asija? If so please call me on: 00 49 1748 526368. Excuse me, please...

Hello? Hello? Is there anyone there? I have no idea who you are, I'm Aleksandar Krsmanović, student, grandson, refugee, long hair, big ears, looking for his memory. Looking for a girl. Well, a woman, really. Asija. Do you know Asija? I once met a madman, a soldier looking for a girl called Emina. Do you know a girl called Asija? I'm conducting a methodical search. My method is to gloss over my own story and draw up endless lists. 00 49 1748 526368.

Asija? Asija? Asija? Asija. Asija. Asija.
    One day a man who asked good questions asked:
Who is that, what is that? Forgive me!
        Where is it,
        Where does it come from,
        Where is it going,
        This country
        Of Bosnia?

Tell me!
And the man he was addressing swiftly replied:
There is a country called Bosnia somewhere, forgive me,
A cold, bleak country,
Naked and hungry,
And besides all that,
Forgive me,
It is defiant
With sleep.

This is me, Aleksandar. The poem is by Mak Dizdar. If you pick it up, call me on: 00 49 1748 526368. I'd like to tell you the story of the baker who sprinkled thirty sacks of flour over the streets of Višegrad one summer night in '92, and after that, in her little shop, she...

From *How the Soldier Repairs the Gramophone* by **Saša Stanišić**, translated from the German by Anthea Bell (Weidenfeld & Nicolson 2008)

How the Soldier Repairs the Gramophone is not so much a novel about the Bosnian conflict as a speculation on the relationship between war and the possibilities of language. For Aleksandar Krsmanović, life is endowed with a mythic quality, and calamity to be dealt with by storytelling. His storytelling talent is tested when war spreads to his home town of Višegrad and he discovers that, although escape is also possible, in fleeing to Germany he remains haunted by the stories he left behind.

Saša Stanišić was born in the Bosnian town of Višegrad and has been living in Germany since 1992. *How the Soldier Repairs the Gramophone* is his first novel, and was shortlisted for the German Book Award, won several other major awards including the Ingeborg Bachmann Prize, and has been translated into twenty-four languages.

Anthea Bell was born in Suffolk and educated at Somerville College, Oxford. She has been a translator from French and German for many years. She has received a number of prizes and awards for her translations which include works of non-fiction, literary and popular fiction, and children's books. She was awarded an OBE in 2010 for services to literature. She lives in Cambridge.

Idle years

Off we went. We eventually found the docks and walked around all the tobacco warehouses there. And, sure enough, by lunchtime, there was Nejip, standing in front of us, covered in a filthy brown layer of muck. He stank of tobacco. He could not believe his eyes. He hugged me, hugged Gazi, then hugged me again. Then he went inside a warehouse and asked for a short break. He shoved us into the restaurant next door and told us to have ourselves a good meal.

'I've got to get back now,' he said, 'but when you're finished here you can wait for me at the café. I'll have a word, so don't you pay for anything!'

Gazi had already sat down. 'Don't just stand there,' he said to me. 'Sit down, and let's tuck in!' He impatiently tapped his fork on his plate.

'Let's not get too carried away,' I warned, 'because…'

'Leave me alone. I'm so hungry I can't see straight. Waiter, excuse me, over here…. These waiters are a bit dozy… Hey, waiter, over here'

The waiter came over.

'First,' said Gazi, 'bring me some cold dolma… Or, no, wait. I'll have hot dolma, but make sure the chef gives me some big ones!'

The waiter chuckled as he went off.

'What are you staring at?' Gazi asked me. 'I'm going to eat a week's worth. What's it to you? But how did Nejip know we were hungry? Do we look that starved, I wonder? That's what you call a friend. One look at us, and he could tell we were hungry. Good on him!'

The waiter brought his dolma.

'I'll have a bowl of soup, please,' I said.

Nejip came over much later when his shift was done. The streets were full of tobacco workers and their hubbub. I would love to have been one of their rusty-brown, dirty but none the less cheerful crowd.

Nejip kept asking us questions, laughing and being happy. 'We can go and see some games. You wouldn't believe some of the matches they have. Which club are you going to go to? I'd say you should get yourselves into Fenerbahçe. You see Fenerbahçe…'

Gazi and I exchanged glances and smiled to ourselves.

'So which hotel are you staying in?' Nejip asked, after we'd had God knows how many coffees. 'Is it a nice, clean place?'

Gazi winked at me. 'Very clean,' he said.

'Well, you can stay with me for tonight anyway. Come on then… Do we have to let the hotel know?'

'Not really,' said Gazi and burst out laughing. 'What hotel, mate? How would we be in a hotel? We've been lucky to have a floor to crash on!'

'Whose floor have you been crashing on?'

'We met this guy called Nevzat. We're on the floor in his room.'

'He shovels coal for a living.'

'And I thought that…' Nejip began and then stopped. He started walking off and beckoned to us to follow.

Well, whatever he had thought, it didn't stop him being the perfect host.

We accompanied him along some streets, around a few corners, entered a crowded neighbourhood with lots of tiled roofs and bay windows and then into his family's small wooden house. He led us into their sitting-room. The house was shady and cool inside. A white, fleeting image of a woman flickered to and fro, first at one end of the room, then at the other.

The cover of the divan and the curtains in the room had been delicately embroidered in greens and pinks and purples. There were no pictures on any of the walls, just thickly framed large, ornate texts in Arabic.

'My mother won't allow photographs in this room,' explained Nejip, 'because she prays here.'

The floorboards were yellow from years of polishing. I could see the side of a hill out of the window, occupied by a graveyard.

We respectfully kissed Nejip's ageing mother's wrinkled hands. She spoke a little Turkish. She asked us polite questions, as best she could, and we tried to provide answers.

It was getting dark. Nejip's sister, who also worked in the tobacco warehouse, entered the room wearing blue earrings and with her curly hair uncovered. 'Welcome,' she said and went and lit the pink lamp on the sideboard before leaving us again.

Before long we were joined by Nejip's dark-moustachioed father, his plaster-splattered uncle and his elder brother, who turned out to be a carpenter. They all had thick and calloused hands and chatted to us in their broken Turkish. I thought they were wonderful people, particularly the father. He talked about various matters, smoothed his thick moustache in an authoritative manner and swore frequently. Meanwhile Nejip's sister laid out a dining-cloth across the floor, laid a chopping-board down on it, set down little flannels we would be using as napkins and brought in the bread-box. She did all this as if playing a little game, smiling now and then and revealing a sparkling gold tooth whenever she did so. I wondered who she was smiling for: me or Gazi?

After we had eaten our meal, drunk our coffees and chatted about things of no consequence, we retired to the beds Nejip's sister had made up for us. Our beds had been laid out side by side. All the bedding was spotlessly clean, expertly patched here and there and smelling of soap.

We climbed into our beds.

'Ahhh…' I sighed. 'This is great!'

Gazi lifted his head up. 'What? You mean the girl? I could get engaged to her immediately!'

I got very cross with him. 'You unscrupulous…'

'No, that's what you are! Now, I know that if I don't beat you to it…'

'What?'

'Come on, I saw you. Giving her all those leery looks.'

The next morning we had a marvellous breakfast and wandered down to Galata. The day passed.

'Once the money from your aunt comes through,' said Gazi the next day, 'we can invite Nejip out.'

'Yes, that'll be good. We can take him out for a meal.'

'To a decent place. With raki and proper meze.'

'We'll pay back Nevzat, too.'

'Obviously. We'll also have to invite him out as well.'

'We could do that, you know. Take him along to a restaurant with Nejip. We ought to, really.'

'We could order two full bottles of raki…'

'If I get about a hundred and fifty or so, then it really won't matter.'

'I wouldn't worry. Your aunt's bound to send you at least that. Because she does know you have a friend with you as well…'

That evening Nevzat handed me the letter I had long been waiting for. I excitedly ripped open the envelope. Gazi and I leaned over and swiftly read the brief note.

I was to leave any so-called friend and come over straight away. There would be no need for me to pay the bus fare – I had only to give my uncle's name. And when was I going to learn not to let every bum and scrounger tag along wherever I went!

Gazi had changed colour. I tore up the letter and threw it out of the window and into the smell of fried fish. First, we sold my clothes and then my suitcase.

'Istanbul is one of a kind!'

You can hop off its trams, hop on to its taxis and entertain whom you want at the restaurant of your choice.... You can set up a factory, or stay unemployed or open a bank... Whatever you want!

'Istanbul is one of a kind!'

Then what?

Well, then, it was first one bit of work, then another. We worked as waiters in cafés around Galata, shovelled coal, did a bit of street selling and occasionally played for some of the useless local football teams, all for no more than a square meal.

'Istanbul is one of a kind!'

Finally one morning, half starving, we bade farewell to the bridge, to the trams, to the dirty sea, to Galata and to Beyoglu and boarded a ship back home, leaving all those beautiful women to the men of Istanbul.

Farewell, then, Istanbul!

We saw Hasan Hüseyin the night we got back to Adana. We found out that my girlfriend had gone off with a sailor. Gazi's had got engaged to her cousin who worked as a farmhand in a nearby village, and the Cretan café owner had been busted for dealing hashish and was doing time.

'How about that?' mused Gazi. 'Would you believe it?'

As for me... 'What are you thinking?' Hasan asked me.

'Don't mind him,' said Gazi. 'He just can't let things go. I don't know what it is with him – you can't dwell on these things.'

It was nearly midnight by the time I left them. I went over to the old sycamore tree, where we used to light matches and signal our girlfriends. It seemed to be waiting patiently, resigned to whatever fate might bring. I leaned against its trunk. In the distance I saw the two brightly lit windows. It all looked exactly the way we had left it. I gave a loud whistle. I noticed two shadows pause at one of the windows. My second whistle created more of a stir. One of the shadows seemed to climb on the sofa. A lamp signalled 'Coming!' My face began to twitch, and my left ear started to hum. I thought of how she would break down and apologize... How on earth was she going to explain what she had done to me? How, I wondered? Just how?

She came and stood in front of me without even saying 'Welcome back.' We stood silently for a while.

'Is it true?' I asked eventually.

She remained quiet.

'So it is true?'

Still nothing.

'How did you meet him?' I asked.

She still didn't say a word.

'So,' I said, 'I don't have a chance.'

She raised her head and looked up to the stars, then folded her arms in front of her chest.

'There's no way he could love you the way I do,' I said. 'You're going to regret this, believe me. You're really going to regret it.'

She shrugged.

I flicked away the last of my cigarette and left.

Back on the tarmac I walked under the electric lights, hearing the occasional whistle of a night-watchman. As I went around a corner someone caught up with me and grabbed me by the arm. It was Hasan.

'Is all this nonsense over now?' he enquired.

I couldn't bring myself to say yes.

'Hey, I'm asking you... Is it all over?'

'You see...'

'Look, mate. There are no ifs or buts about it. You've got to get your act together. You've either got to go back to school or get yourself a proper job.'

'Got a light?' I lit a cigarette.

—

From *The Idle Years* by **Orhan Kemal**, translated from the Turkish by Cengiz Lugal (Peter Owen 2008)

Orhan Kemal is one of Turkey's best-loved writers. This volume contains *My Father's House* and *The Idle Years*, the first two semi-autobiographical novels in a series, set in the 1920s and 1930s when Turkey was undergoing major social change. The unnamed narrator grows up in an affluent household in an Adana village. The family are forced to migrate to Beirut as the father falls foul of the authorities and there the narrator develops into a rebel while he reluctantly attempts to support a now impoverished family.

Orhan Kemal – the pen name of Mehmet Rasit Ö˘gütçü – was born in Adana in 1914. His father's political activism led the family to emigrate to Syria and Lebanon. Time spent with the celebrated writer Nazım Hikmet in the Bursa State Prison had an important influence on Kemal's socialist political stance. He moved to Istanbul in 1951 and concentrated on his writing, producing more than thirty novels and story collections as well as plays and film scripts. He died in 1970.

Cengiz Lugal produced this translation for the Orhan Kemal Foundation, and it was subsequently edited for the book's UK publication.

The chill of the city

It's freezing in this *bled*, the wind makes my eyes stream, and I'm legging it to keep warm. Wrong place to live, is what I'm thinking, the climate's not right, because deep down it's just a question of climate, and this morning the crazy cold of France is paralysing me.

I'm Ahlème, by the way, and I'm walking through the crush of all these people in a rush, bumping into each other, running late, arguing, on their mobiles, not smiling, and I can see my brothers who are so cold, like me. I can always spot them, it's something in their eyes, like they want to be invisible, or somewhere else. But they're here.

I never complain at home, not even when our heating cuts out, because Dad just goes: 'You keep quiet now, you didn't live through the winter of '63.' Not much I can say to that, in 1963 I wasn't even born. So I shuffle and slide along France's slippery streets, passing Rue Joubert where a few prostitutes on the pavements call out to each other. They look like beat-up old dolls who aren't afraid of the cold any more. Working girls are the climatic exception, it doesn't matter where they are, they've stopped feeling anything.

My appointment with the temping agency is for 10.40 a.m. Not 45. Not 30. Things are kind of precise here in France, where every minute counts, and it's something I'll never get used to. I was born on the other side of the sea, and the African minute contains a lot more than sixty seconds.

Mr Miloudi, the youth adviser in my area, suggested I apply to this new outfit: Temp Plus.

Miloudi's old skool. He's been running the youth advisory service on Uprising Estate since back in the day, and he's seen all the ASBOs in our endz. He's efficient, I guess. But he's always in a hurry. So it wasn't like there was any hanging around in my interview:

'Sit down, young lady…'

'Thank you.'

'And next time, please remember to knock before entering.'

'Sorry, I wasn't thinking.'

'I'm only saying it for your own benefit, you can fail an interview for that kind of thing.'

'I'll remember.'

'Good, let's get going, no time to waste, we've only got a twenty-minute slot. You need to fill out the skills form in front of you, write in block capitals in the boxes, and don't make any spelling mistakes. If you're not sure about a word, ask me for the dictionary. Did you bring your CV?'

'Yes. Five copies, like you said.'

'Very good. There's the form, fill it out carefully. I'll be back in five minutes.'

He took a box of kitchen matches out of his pocket, together with a pack of Marlboros, and walked away, leaving me to face my destiny. There were piles of files on his desk, forms everywhere I looked, taking up all the space. And a giant clock fixed to the wall.

Each time its hands moved, it made a noise that echoed in my ears like someone ringing the end of time. I felt hot all of a sudden. Mental block. The five minutes sped by like a TGV, and all I'd written was my surname, my first name and my date of birth.

I could hear Mr Miloudi's dry cough in the corridor; he was coming back.

'So? Where are you up to? Have you finished?'

'No. Not yet.'

'But you haven't filled in anything!' he complained, leaning over the piece of paper.

'I didn't get time.'

'There are plenty of people waiting for an appointment, I have other clients after you, as you saw in the waiting room. We've only got ten minutes to contact the SREP now, because at this time of year there's no point going via AGPA, there won't be any places left. I suggest we try for paid training at the FAJ.... Why can't you fill it out? It's straightforward enough.'

'I don't know what to put in the 'life plans' box...'

'You must have some idea.'

'No.'

'I can see from your CV that you've had plenty of professional experience, there must be something there you enjoyed.'

'Those were casual jobs, like being a waitress or a shop assistant. They were about money, Mr Miloudi, not my life plan.'

'Okay, let's leave the application form for now, we haven't got time. I'm going to give you the address of another temping agency, while we're waiting to hear from the FAJ.'

Johanna at Temp Plus looks sixteen, her voice trembles and it's painful trying to make out what she's saying. I get that she's asking me to fill out a questionnaire. She gives me a biro with her office's stupid logo on it and asks me to follow her. She's wearing these extra-stretchy jeans that show up all the times she's stuffed her face instead of sticking to her Weight Watchers' diet – they make her look like she's having an affair or something.

She points to a seat by a small table where I'm meant to sit down. It's difficult to write, my fingers are frozen stiff, I'm finding it hard to unclench them. It reminds me of when Dad – the Boss, we call him – used to come home from work. He always needed a bit of time before he could open his hands. 'It's because of the pneumatic drill,' he used to say.

I scribble, I fill in their boxes, I tick and sign. Everything on their application form is teeny-tiny and their questions are bordering on the annoying. No, I'm not married, no I haven't got any kids, or a driving licence, no I didn't go on to higher education, no I'm not registered disabled and no I'm not French. In fact, where's the box for: 'My life's FLOPPED'? That way, I'll just tick it, end of story.

Johanna, whose jeans are so tight they're cutting up into her crotch, puts on this sympathetic voice and offers me my first temping 'assignment'. It's funny how they call them 'assignments'. Makes shitty jobs seem like an adventure.

She's offering me stocktaking out in Leroy Merlin next Friday evening. I say yes, straight up, I need the work so badly I'd take almost anything.

I come out of there feeling well pleased with myself, which just goes to show it doesn't take much.

Then I head off to join Linda and Nawel at the Cour de Rome, which is a café in the Saint-Lazare area, near to the agency. They've been trying to see me for a few weeks now, but to be honest I mostly avoid going out when I haven't got any money. Plus these days they're glued to their boyfriends, which is kind of boring, and I always feel so clumsy plonked in between them. I'm not far off winning the European and African Championships for Best Female Gooseberry.

The girls are sitting on the bench at the back of the café. Typical, bunch of smokers hiding away, I know their old tricks by heart. They even set up this HQ in our endz where they used to hang out behind the stadium, to bill up one, and the code to meet was: 'Anyone fancy keeping fit?'

They're dressed to kill, nothing new there. I've noticed how slick they always look, and I'm thinking how can they spend so much time getting dressed, doing their hair and make-up? Nothing's left to chance, everything matches, it's all calculated and chosen carefully.

It's not often I sign up to making the effort, but when I do it nearly kills me, it's too much like hard work if you ask me. What wouldn't us girls do for an admiring look or a compliment on a bad-hair day? So if someone says she's gone all out with the garms just to please herself it's like, yeah right!

I'm level with the girls now and they light their cigarettes in sync, welcoming me with a warm smoky 'hi'.

Sticking to the rules, a 'wassup?' follows hot on its heels, and we always leave a bit of space to think about this before kicking off the discussion.

Then comes the question I've been dreading.

'Any new boyfriends to tell us about?' A shake of the head, they get the idea. How come they always ask about boyfriends, plural? I mean, it's hard enough finding one person you like, so why complicate things?

Next up, same old: 'So what's a *fine* girl like you doing still single? Your problem is, you don't really want a boyfriend.... You've only got yourself to blame, you're too choosy. We've set you up with some fit guys, we're talking bare buff beasts for real, there's nothing else we can do for you, you're shut off.'

I can never get them to understand it's not as bad as they're making out because, if things work out, it's not like I'll be going through the menopause tomorrow. But they just keep on busting a gut to introduce me to total plonkers. We're talking guys with an IQ of 2 who are so up themselves it's unreal, or else complete tossers, or wastemans who can't string two words together, or manic depressives.

So, I do this nifty manoeuvre to get them to change the subject – I've got a real talent for dodging obstacles and problems, three times African and European champion.

Basically, I reckon the girls have already decided on their life plan, same as most people, it's all mapped out in their heads, like pieces of a jigsaw waiting to fit together. They divide their time between their J.O.B. and leisure, they go on holiday to the same place every summer, they always buy the same brand of deodorant, their families are chilled and they've got long-term boyfriends. In fact, even their guys are spotless, I mean, I like them and everything, but you wouldn't catch me going away with them for a weekend. No flies there. Plus they come from the same village as the girls, back in the *bled*, so their parents are bare haps. It's like incest is back in fashion. At least if it's your brother, you can be sure he comes from exactly the same place as you, just ask your mum. The girls reckon it's practical, because if the families came from different traditions, they wouldn't agree on everything; and another thing, it makes bringing up the kids more complicated if you don't speak the same language.... If you ask me, they're just stupid details, and you don't set up home together just because it's practical.

Nawel's back from holiday; she was in Algeria staying with her dad's family, and I tell her she's lost loads of weight, at least five kilos. 'Yeah? Am I really skinny?'

'You've dried up, for real. People'll feel sorry for you, *miskina*!'

'That's going back to the *bled* for you.'

'Diet holiday, innit.'

'Yeah, for real... All that heat, stringy beans every meal, your gran's jokes, Chilean soap operas.... Course you're gonna lose weight.'

'How did you do it?' asks Linda, she's curious now. 'Two whole months in the *bled*, I'd have got depressed, straight up.'

'I guess the time just goes. But the TV, man, that was ova-wack, there's only one channel. Even Mr Bean is censored over there.'

'At least you don't get embarrassing stuff like the whole tribe in front of the telly and bam! a hot scene flashes up, or one of those shower gel ads. You get me, the old man starts coughing and you've got to grab that remote and zap, fast as. That's why we've got a satellite dish round ours now. It's saved our lives because on French TV they RATE all the girls getting their kit off, and it's like totally random.'

'How was it staying with your family?'

'Bunch of scavengers more like.... The first week, they loved us up because our suitcases were bulging. But as soon as we'd handed out all the presents that was it, our ratings dropped. I said to my mum: 'Next summer, I swear on the Koran, let's just get Tati to sponsor us, it'd make life a lot easier.'

Coming up, it's time for the neighbourhood gossip with Linda.com. She's too much, this girl, a total blabbermouth. Linda knows everything about everybody, I don't get how she does it, sometimes she even knows what's going on with people before they do.

'You know Tony Lopez...?'

'No, who's he?'

'Yes you do, the new guy at number 16.'

'The blond one?'

'Nah, tall guy with brown hair. Works at Midas.'

'Yeah, what about him?'

'He's going out with Gwendolyn!'

'What, that short girl? The redhead in your block?'

'No, not her. The anorexic with loads of half-finished tattoos. Nawel, you know who I mean...'

'Yeah, got you, I see her on the bus on the way to my J.O.B. So how come she never got her tattoos finished? I've always wondered about that.'

'How's Linda supposed to know that?' I ask, me being naïve.

'Yeah, yeah, I know this one...'

'Shit, man, you've got all the tabloid. Spit it out.'

'So, she was with this dodgy guy before, right, a tattoo artist. Well, that's it, innit. He starts on her tattoos and then he never gets to finish them because he dumps her for another girl.'

'Bastard. He could of finished the job.'

'So anyway, Anorexia's going out with Tony Lopez, and then what?'

'Well, he wanted to leave her. According to my sources, it's because he's sticking it in the accountant round at Midas. But seeing as Gwendolyn ova-LIKES him, she did all this psychological pressure shit to make him stay. So that's what he ended up doing and then he had to pay for it big time...'

'Meaning? Spit it out! Cut the tacky suspense.'

'Wifey only goes and makes a kid behind his back. Like, she's preggo out to *here*. Crazy, innit?'

Every time, Linda signs off with: 'Crazy, innit?'

Before going our separate ways, we told each other a few more stories, the kind you tell in hushed voices, and the same smile that gave away a few of our secrets is protecting me now against the big chill of the outside world.

The platform's black with people, *severe delays occurring*. One train in four, that's what they said on the radio.

No choice, I'm gripping the overhead bar in the carriage. No air in this RER, people are pushing me, crushing me. The train is sweating and I'm feeling choked by all these sad bodies craving colour. All the air in Africa wouldn't be enough for them. They're ghosts, and they're all sick, contaminated with sadness.

I head back to Ivry to help my neighbour, Auntie Mariatou, and her children. My asthmatic RER spits me out into our endz, where it's even colder. Days like today, you don't know where you're going any more, you're clean out of luck, too bad, I guess. Yeah, it's sad, but luckily, deep down, there's still this little thing that helps you get up in the morning. There's no guarantee, but you hold out for it getting better one day. Like Auntie says: 'The best stories have the worst beginnings.'

From **Dreams From the Endz** by **Faïza Guène**, translated from the French by Sarah Ardizzone (Chatto & Windus 2008)

Dreams from the Endz, Faïza Guène's second novel, illuminates the impact of French politics on everyday lives. Her heroine is 24-year-old Ahlème, who struggles with her family as well as the struggles and queues that come with being an immigrant, and the guilt-trips of distant relatives 'back home'. But when she returns after a ten-year absence to the country where her mother was massacred at a village wedding, she brokers a kind of truce, both with her homeland, and with the imposed need to forge a future.

   Faïza Guène was born in France in 1985 to Algerian parents. Her first novel, *Just Like Tomorrow*, written when she was 17 years old, was a huge success in France, selling almost 400,000 copies, and was translated around the world. She lives at Pantin, Seine-Saint-Denis, a suburb north of Paris.

Sarah Ardizzone won the 2005 Marsh Award for her translation of Daniel Pennac's *Eye of the Wolf* and the 2007 Scott-Moncrieff Prize for Faïza Guène's *Just Like Tomorrow*.

The armies

Like me, my wife is a teacher, also retired: the Secretary of Education owes us each ten months' worth of pension payments. She taught in a school in San Vicente – she was born and raised there, a town six hours from this one, where I was born. I met her in San Vicente, forty years ago, in the bus terminal, which in those days was an enormous corrugated-zinc shed. There I saw her, surrounded by sacks of fruit and orders of cornbread, dogs, pigs and hens, amid the exhaust of the motors and the prowling of the passengers waiting for their buses to leave. I saw her sitting alone on a wrought-iron bench, with room for two. I was dazzled by her dreamy black eyes, her wide forehead, her narrow waist, the ample backside under a pink skirt. The white, short-sleeved, linen blouse showed off her fine, pale arms and the intense darkness of her nipples. I went over and sat down beside her, as if levitating, but she immediately stood up, pretended to fix her hair, gave me a sidelong glance and walked away, feigning interest in the notices outside the transport office.

Then something happened which distracted my attention from her uncommon rustic beauty; only such an incident could wrench my eyes from her: on the next bench was a much older man, rather fat, dressed in white; his hat was white too, as was the handkerchief poking out from behind his lapel; he was eating ice cream – just as white – clearly anxious; the colour white was stronger than my love at first sight: too much white, also the thick drops of sweat soaking his bullish neck; all of him trembled, and that was in spite of being directly beneath the fan; his hefty body took up the whole bench, he was sprawled out, absolute master of his world; on the fingers of each hand he wore silver rings; there was a leather briefcase beside him, overflowing with documents; he gave the impression of total innocence: his blue eyes wandered distractedly all over the place: sweet and calm, they looked me over once but did not give me a second glance. And then another man, exactly the opposite, young and bone-jutting thin, barefoot, in a T-shirt and frayed shorts, walked up to him, put a revolver to his forehead and pulled the trigger. The cloud of smoke from the barrel was enough to envelop me; it was like a dream for everyone, including the fat man, who blinked and, at the moment of the shot, looked as though he still wanted to enjoy his ice cream. The one with the revolver fired only once; the fat man slid to one side, without falling, his eyes closed, as if he had all of a sudden fallen asleep, abruptly dead, but without letting go of his ice cream; the murderer threw the gun far away – a gun that no-one made any attempt to look for or pick up – and walked unhurriedly out of the bus station, without anyone stopping him. Except that a few seconds before throwing the gun away he looked at me, the fat man's nearest neighbour: never before in my life had I been struck by such a dead look; it was as if someone made of stone were looking at me: his gaze made me think he was going to shoot at me until he had emptied the chamber. And that was when I saw: the murderer was not a young man at all; he must have been no more than eleven or twelve. He was a child. I never knew if they followed him or caught him, and I never tried to find out; after all it was not so much his look that nauseated me: it was the physical horror of discovering that he was a child.

A child, and that must have been why I was more afraid, and with reason, but also without reason, that he would kill me too. I fled from him, from where he had been, hunted for the bus station toilet, not yet knowing whether to piss or vomit, while the cry went up all about. Several men gathered round the corpse, no-one decided to give chase to the murderer: either we were all afraid, or it did not really seem to matter to anyone. I went into the lavatory: it was a small space with broken opaque mirrors, and at the back, the only cubicle looked like a crate – also made of corrugated-zinc sheets, like the terminal itself. I went and pushed the door and saw her just as she was sitting down, her dress bunched up around her waist, two thighs as pale as they were naked narrowing in terror. I said an anguished and heartfelt 'Pardon me' and immediately closed the door at a speed calculated to allow me to take another look at her, the implacable roundness of her rump bursting out from under the hitched up skirt, her near nudity, her eyes – a rumble of fear and surprise and a hint of remote pleasure in the light of her pupils at knowing herself admired; of that I am now sure. And fate: we were assigned adjoining seats on the dilapidated bus that would take us to the capital.

A long trip, more than eighteen hours, awaited us: the pretext to listen to each other was the death of the fat man in white in the terminal; I felt her arm brush against my arm, but also all of her fear, her indignation, the whole heart of the woman who would be my wife. And the coincidence: we shared the same profession, who could have imagined? Two educators, forgive me for asking, what is your name? (silence), my name is Ismael Pasos, and you? (silence), she was only listening, but finally: 'My name is Otilia del Sagrario Aldana Ocampo.' The same hopes. Soon the murder and the incident in the toilet were forgotten – but only apparently, because they went on recurring, becoming associated, in an almost absurd way, in my memory: first death, then nakedness.

Today my wife, ten years younger than me, is sixty, but she looks older, she moans and walks hunched over. She is not the same girl she was at twenty sitting down on a public toilet, her eyes like lighthouse beams over the hitched up island, the join of her legs, the triangle of her sex – indescribable animal – no. Now she is old, happy indifference, going from here to there, in the middle of her country and its war, busy with her house, the cracks in the walls, the possible leaks in the roof, although the shouts of the war burst in her ears, she is just like everyone, when it comes right down to it, and I am happy for her happiness, and if she loved me today as much as she does her fish and her cats perhaps I would not be peering over the wall.

Perhaps.

—

From *The Armies* by **Evelio Rosero**, translated from the Spanish by Anne McLean (MacLehose Press 2008)

In *The Armies* Evelio Rosero creates a vivid, relentless narrative often as violent as the events it describes. Ismael, a retired teacher, spends his mornings gathering oranges in the sunshine and spying on his neighbour as she sunbathes naked in her garden. Returning from a walk one morning, he finds that his wife has disappeared. When gunfire signals the approach of war, he cannot leave, and becomes an unwilling witness to violence that sweeps through his country.

In Colombia **Evelio Rosero's** work has been recognized by the National Literature Award, and in Britain *The Armies* won the 2009 Independent Foreign Fiction Prize. Rosero is the author of seven novels and two collections of short stories, as well as several books for children and young adults.

Anne McLean has translated books by authors including Julio Cortázar, Tomás Eloy Martínez and Juan Gabriel Vásquez. Her translations of novels by Javier Cercas have been short-listed for the 2008 International IMPAC Dublin Literary Award and awarded the 2004 Independent Foreign Fiction Prize and the Premio Valle Inclán. Her translation of *The Armies* won her a second Independent Foreign Fiction Prize in 2009.

The end of Freddy

At this point my much respected readers should be asked if they've ever heard of a gentleman called Rácz. Of course, this is purely a rhetorical question, because if the reader in his boundless kindness has already reached for this modest book, then the author will not be presumptuous in assuming that the name of Rácz is not totally unfamiliar to the reader.

This literary hero's faithful supporters and admirers will certainly be pleased to be told that, in my imagination, he is still having an excellent time. His hotels, restaurants, pizzerias, and casinos prosper just as they did in previous *Rivers of Babylon* books. He is doing equally well in other business activities. Since he is an influential man and knows how to win over similarly influential people, he has managed to privatise successfully some lucrative businesses. Take, for example, the once famous Stupava brewery that was recently going broke. Rácz bought it for peanuts and everybody thought that he was going to asset-strip it. But not Rácz. Not this time. Beer, unlike banking or insurance business, really amused him. He didn't strip its assets: on the contrary, he surrounded himself by experts and invested in new technology. The quality of Stupavar 11º, once so popular, went up. It won a prize at the Agrokomplex Fair and even got a gold medal at the Munich Beer Festival. Using sophisticated media campaigns he taught people how to drink Stupavar. And their new product, the dark beer Mast 16º? It flies off the shelves even in the Czech lands. And that is, as they say, something.

Rácz is no great beer expert. When he needed experts, he bought them. He doesn't drink much beer. He watches his weight. The slightest hint of a paunch is quickly dealt with in his home fitness room. He prefers good whisky, the best. He has been faithful to the Chivas Regal brand for many years, but won't say no to other reputable brands either.

'It's not only Scotland where they know how to distil a good whisky! Not just *Heevash Reygahl*!' he remarks and taps a bottle labelled Single Malt. 'Malta, too! This Maltese one is quite good!'

Lately, he's acquired a taste for cognac. If you want to please him, give him a bottle of XO. He's sure to appreciate it.

Someone once brought him a bottle of a valuable old Armagnac. Rácz thanked him, so as not to offend the donor, but secretly gave the bottle to his chief bodyguard, Mozoň. 'Rácz drinks only French cognac!' he declared condescendingly. 'Armenian cognac, from what used to be Russia, is only good for ex-secret policemen.'

Rácz never refuses a good bourbon, either. 'It doesn't always have to be just Scottish or Maltese whisky,' he says. 'Even the French can make a good one. Their bourbon's not bad at all.'

So much about Rácz's consumer habits.

He enjoys living in the luxury villa above the city. He's not often to be found there, however. You're more likely to find him in the Hotel Ambassador Rácz, where he has his office.

If he manages to get home early occasionally, he devotes himself to his family. It's his temple and his refuge in the rough seas of the mundane duties and worries of a major businessman and a man of power. His beautiful, intelligent wife Lenka has borne him two sons: the older, Karol, and the younger, Attila. The boys are bright; they study well. Next year, Karol will go to an élite boarding school in Great Britain.

Karol doesn't like the idea. His friends are here, and he can brag in school about his father. In England, they'll all be like him. Maybe he'll turn out to be the poorest one of all.

In a moment of weakness he confides in his father.

Rácz's eyes almost pop out of his face.

'There's no way Rácz's son is going to be a poor man!' he roars.

Then he calms down. He will put a kind, but stern mask on his face. Karol shouldn't brag about his father's accomplishments. He should brag about what he's going to achieve himself. If he does achieve anything. A bit of modesty never hurt anyone.

Karol's mother joins in. She sides with his father, but she supports her son as well. Now she's unhappy at the idea of losing him for a while. She tries to move the goalposts. She repeats that the boy is sensitive and afraid of being alone. He's eight now and even today he gets into their bed whenever he has a bad dream. Doesn't Rácz love him?

Rácz frowns. Now he has two rivals. He wants his sons to be tough, educated and manly. Not cissies. Yes, he does love Karol; after all he is his first-born son. He loves Attila, the younger one, too. And he loves Lenka, too. But Rácz's love is not soppy or soft. His love is tough, demanding, and strict. He doesn't want to feed his sons fish forever. He wants to teach his sons to catch fish. And do it better than anyone else.

Karol can't grasp that. But he senses his mother could stop things happening, including his father's decision. Didn't she tell him he was afraid of being on his own? Yes, being on his own is what he fears. He's afraid of being on his own.

Rácz laughs. Rácz has been alone ever since childhood. He was an orphan, practically. Nobody liked him. Where he comes from, everyone let him down, and, worse, hurt him. Karol needn't bullshit Rácz, his own father. Rácz looks at his wife; her look of reproach bounces back to his eyes. But Rácz has to say it straight. Karol can't use loneliness as a pretext for defiance. He has no idea what real loneliness is, he's just blathering. When Rácz arrived in the city, in *Rivers of Babylon*, he didn't know anyone there. He stuck out like a sore thumb. He lived in a little hovel behind the boiler-room. Everyone treated him like a mug. But he didn't let them. And why not? Because he's no fool. In the end he worked his way to the top. All that time he found only one being he could confide in and who really loved him. Yes, Karol's mother! She even dropped out of university for Rácz's sake. Because she believed in him. And who was he? A shitty stoker! This is how, like a little flower, he climbed out of his basement up to the light. And he finally got to where he is now. Rácz did it; now he wants Karol to do even better. Not to have to travel even one of the thorny paths his father had to take. He simply wants Karol to start where his father passes the baton to him. To take it further. And higher. So he's got to go to that school. With strict discipline. And English, day and night. That's how winners are educated, fucking right!

Karol's cheeks are puffed. He doesn't want to be like his father. He wants to be a musician. He wants to have guitar or drum lessons.

Rácz clutches his head with his hands. Why guitar? Why drums? No one in the Rácz family needs to learn a musical instrument. The Rácz family has enough money to hire people to play for them. Anytime, even at midnight. Karol will go to school, period. Other boys would shriek for joy. There are boys who study shit-all, because their parents haven't got the money. Rácz, for example, only did two years at agricultural college. That's all his education; luckily he has brains. His parents, God rest their souls, were so stingy that he had to eat his bread buttered underneath, so they couldn't see. They had a boiled egg once a year, at Easter. The leftovers on Karol's plate would have kept Rácz alive for a week when he was his age. A week!

Karol is quiet. He stubbornly shakes his head. That school, that Eton, makes you wear uniform.

'So what?' Rácz claps his hands. 'SO WHAT? For Christ's sake! Rácz had to wear overalls all his childhood. Handed down from his father. Even to school. That was his uniform. In summer he went barefoot, in winter he wore rubber boots. He used to stuff them with newspapers, and wrapped his feet in newspaper, too, to stop his toes freezing. Luckily, down south, the winters aren't so bad. Uniforms? That's what Rácz really appreciates. They'll finally make a man out of Karol. No more of those revolting baggy jeans, baggy tee shirts and expensive trainers three sizes too big. By the way, talking about trainers, would Karol kindly tie his shoelaces? Rácz can't stand the sight of them. He's waiting. That's more like it. Otherwise Karol might step on his shoelace and, since he walks about with his head in the clouds like a zombie, he could easily fall, hit his head, and get even more stupid than he is now! And those horrible baseball caps! The peak was meant to keep out the sun. So why is Karol's cap turned round with the peak at the back? He looks like some kind of Jew. And anyway, why does he wear that cap, if it's a baseball cap? Does Karol play baseball? Has he ever held a baseball bat in his hand? No, he's clumsy at everything. What a bungler! In England, that school is sure to have baseball, too. He'll learn how to play and right away he'll find out what that cap is for.

Rácz hopes that his son will at least be happy about that. But Karol is not the sporty type. He's still in a huff.

And Karol can kindly straighten his back, Rácz orders. They'll teach him in that school. Twenty hours of P.E. a week. Karol needn't make faces. There won't be any staff there, no servants, no cleaning woman over there: Karol will have to do everything for himself. And not only for himself, but for others, too, because the first year he will have to be a fag for the older boys. He heard the first time. That's how it is in English boarding schools. Bullying. But Karol mustn't let it get him down: that's nothing compared to the bullying that Rácz put up with in army service. Lešany near Prague. Military unit 5963, third artillery regiment, seventh battery. That was army service! And he survived. Because he was what? Because he was no fool, but tough and honest, as well.

Rácz smiles and lights a cigar. He puts his arm round his stubborn son's shoulders and walks with him through the big French windows onto the spacious terrace. With his free hand, a cigar between his fingers, he traces an arc over the city's illuminated night panorama.

'If you cope with all that,' he tells his son, 'when humility, self-denial, and hard physical and psychological demands make a better person of you, then you'll come back here and all this will be yours.'

The same way as it now belongs to Rácz.

As a sign of togetherness, he slaps his son on the back.

'May I go inside now?' Karol asks, still in a huff.

'Clear off,' says Rácz: he feels let down, shrouds himself in smoke and shreds in his hand an eight-hundred-crown Romeo y Julieta cigar.

The panorama of the city is breathtaking. Rácz searches out the lights of the buildings that he owns and slowly calms down. He has been having difficulties lately with distant vision. Everything looks foggy. If he squints, he can see well, but he sees everything double. Rácz is beginning to worry. Could he possibly need glasses? Rácz always used to have an eagle's eyesight.

Luckily the buildings of the hotels Ambassador Rácz I and II are so prominent that the hotelier can effortlesly rest his admiring gaze on them. For a while Rácz plunges into memories. He recalls the times when he was a nobody, stoking the Hotel Ambassador. Gradually working his way up to be the king of the money-changers and a powerful man. And later buying the hotel at auction, surrounding himself with reliable people, and harshly sorting out the Albanian mafia. Yes, Rácz is a big boss, admired and feared. They all obey his every word. Word? They obey if he raises an eyebrow. It's only in his own family that he can't keep order. He's too soft.

In the evening, accompanied by two guards, he drives into town. He enters the Hotel Ambassador, walks through the lobby, and takes a look at the bar. Then he turns on the computer in his office and checks his various businesses' daily takings. One bodyguard stands outside in the hallway; the other one stands near the door, watching the antechamber on the screen. About midnight, people from Rácz's security company, Sekuritatia, drag in Sabadoš, the owner of a casino in the centre. He has not been paying into the kitty for his security. Rácz's people have kept an eye on him for a while and have now decided to put the squeeze on him.

Rácz asks a guard to pull off Sabadoš's belt. He beats the guilty man with the belt for a long time. When his right hand begins to hurt, he uses his left. When his left begins to hurt, too, he hands the belt to another guard to carry on. Sabadoš's back and buttocks are minced like a hamburger, he's crying like a woman.

As the guard beats him, Rácz watches him without anger. 'Šolík's a kind man,' he tells the victim. 'If you've got kids, he'll bring them up.'

From *The End of Freddy* (volume 3 of the *Rivers of Babylon* trilogy) by **Peter Pišťanek**, translated from the Slovak by Peter Petro (Garnett Press 2008)

Peter Pišťanek's trilogy, *Rivers of Babylon*, was written in the 1990s as Slovak socialism collapsed and capitalism took over. Rácz's first appearance is in autumn 1989: he is the hotel stoker who controls the heating pipes, an idiot of genius, a psychopathic gangster, the face of the future. The novels' publication aroused controversy in Slovakia, but Pišťanek's reputation was assured by their originality and inventiveness, and Slovak readers acknowledged Peter Pišťanek as their most flamboyant and fearless writer, stripping the nation of its myths and false self-esteem.

   Peter Pišťanek was born in 1960. He enrolled in Bratislava's Academy of Performing Arts, but did not graduate, and was also a drummer in a rock group. His breakthrough came in 1991 with *Rivers of Babylon*, the first novel in the trilogy.

Peter Petro is Professor of Russian and East European literature and Chair of Modern European Studies at the University of British Columbia.. He is the author of *Modern Satire: Four Studies* (1982) and *A History of Slovak Literature* (1995), and has translated Martin Šimečka's *The Year of the Frog* and Alexej Fulmek's *Dispatches from the Home Front* (2000).

An artist's model

Saturday, 15 November 1941, Lillestrøm

Sometimes I think I've finished with this diary. I think I've grown out of it, I've grown older. I've said what has to be said. I'm through with myself. I'm so lacking in any illusions I could be forty years old. Why bother writing in that case? There's no richness or excess of feelings that need a release. All that remains of my good and young sides emerges when I'm with Gunvor[†].

I have no idea what purpose these pages might still serve. The fact that I continue to write is more habit than anything else. Capturing a few nice hours to fill the time. So I can say to myself later: I can still write something, about myself, about me, my life. Writing, writing. There's a lot that can be written.

But what exists between Gunvor and me is too sacred to be touched by words. Besides that, there's nothing particular to note. Apart from the that I still have no home. That's old news. When I think of how homeless I am, think of it as an onlooker, then I almost feel sorry for myself.

There's something else I've been meaning to write about for ages. It was in Trondheim. We were coming back from work. We were tired and drawn. We walked down Prinsens gate, boring old Prinsens gate. We were already standing by the entrance to the YWCA. People were crowding around a few German soldiers... and? We approached them. Well, a small German soldier in a green uniform was standing there, railing at a drunken man who couldn't even stand any longer. He was just smiling mischievously, while the German kept on abusing him.

The soldier became irritated. He let the drunken man fall to the ground, who ended up flat on his stomach. The people standing there and watching moved uncomfortably. A young man, slim and with a clever face, stepped forward. I won't forget the expression in his eyes. He said: 'But please...'

The soldier got even more annoyed. He went over to the young man. 'Now just move on.'

The Norwegian man understood German. But he didn't leave. The soldier took another menacing pace towards him and started waving his

---

† Gunvor Hofmo, the Norwegian poet who preserved Ruth Maier's diaries and with whom she had an intense friendship for two years.

hands around in front of his face. 'Don't you understand German?'

The other man opened his eyes wide: 'No. I don't.'

The soldier was fuming now. I thought: No, he won't do anything to him. But he did do something. He hit the man in the face. Wallop!

I could hear a quiet sigh from those who were standing around. But they stood there stiffly, seriously. There were lots of them. The soldier was just one against many. Just him on his own.

The Norwegian's eyes now had a pained expression, and he looked young and gentle. All he said was: 'But please....'

The soldier was led away by other Germans who had arrived.

I found the whole scene terrifying. I cannot recall that anything of this sort has upset me as much as that incident. It was strange: Gunvor didn't find it as terrible as I did.

Another typical occurrence these days. The son of Frau Heltene, our 'leader' in the winter camp in Biri, died on the Eastern Front. He was sixteen years old. I've read his letters: he totally misunderstood National Socialism and idealised it in such a childish manner, and with such enthusiasm, that you can't help but smile. He volunteered for the Waffen SS. He was Frau Heltene's only comfort, her great love.

Hildegard, John and now that. That's how it is every day. Nonetheless it's idiotic to report it as anything but fact. It would also be quite wrong to start thinking in terms of 'holy murder'. I think that it's the same for everybody who reads the daily tally of dead and captured soldiers at breakfast. Feelings are lost. Only from time to time do you think things like: They're murdering each other. Yes. And when is it going to end?... But that's all. We've become so blunted. We're not surprised any more. That's why we're closer to what happens here in Norway.

Even outrage and enthusiasm over some death sentences (and again it's the workers who are being sentenced to death) don't last longer than an hour.

Wednesday, 19 November 1941, Lillestrøm

Facts!

A short list of facts, a Norwegian daily digest?

The food situation.

Bread: few people manage with the ration cards. Those undertaking physically demanding labour get additional rations.

Milk: not rationed until October this year. Now adults receive one-quarter litre, children under ten one litre per day. All the milk goes to Finland, Germany etc. Milk rationing led directly to a number of strikes in Oslo factories, with the result that two Norwegians (Viggo Hansteen, Rolf Wickstrøm) were shot and others sentenced to 'life' imprisonment.

Butter: goes to Germany. Impossible to find dairy butter. Margarine getting ever rarer. People are using whale oil for frying.

Meat: you need cards. (Almost) unobtainable. Probably goes to Germany.

Fish: getting rarer and rarer.

Potatoes: difficult to buy. But people have hoarded them, so it's all right.

Eggs: none.

Chocolate: none (queues).

Cigarettes: none.

Coffee: very little, with ration card. Soon there won't be any coffee ration cards.

Cocoa: none.

Sugar: little, with ration card.

Clothes: clothes card of 300 coupons (a pair of mittens costs 10 coupons).

Shoes: have to apply for them. Application usually approved.

Saturday, 22 November 1941, Lillestrøm

Concerning loneliness. I'm no longer lonely. I have Gunvor. I've staked everything on her. That is why I felt so dreadful when I thought I'd lost her. I cried. I've rarely cried like that. And yet sometimes I long for a man. Without Gunvor I'd never be able to cope without a man. So this man-less-ness is just a gentle pain inside me.

I remember every snippet of conversation I have with men. I love many of the faces of men who walk past. Those that I see in the Deichmann and university libraries.

At the moment Tobben is sitting in the dining room. Frau Strøm's brother. I would love him very much if he only gave me the chance. When he offered me his hand his face felt like a pain to me and I look at him as if he were my lover. Tobben is a very good man. He has such a lovely, calm way of talking, as if he didn't want to hurt people, get too close to them. He said, with a slight singing in his voice, 'So... how are you?'

At that moment I loved him very much.

Sometimes I see Jewish people and they have this completely – how shall I put it? – erotic effect on me. They awaken a feeling of love within me. I feel myself drawn to them. Today I saw a small, tiny Jew. He was from Germany and spoke Norwegian with a German accent. He was talking with a blonde girl who was twice his size. I think he was very lonely because there was a thin, coy smile on his lips. A little soft. He was very ugly. Spectacles, big nose and so short. He said, 'I'm a bookworm.' A crooked smile, then: 'Yes, I am a little nervous.'

Oh, you little Jew. It's an unappealing habit of Jews to say of themselves, 'I'm slightly nervous.'

Another Jew in the library. Also from Germany, tall with a bent back, his whole face turned inwards. Eyes deep below the forehead. Looked somewhat blind and moved nervously as if he had poor sight. Nodded his head.

I love Jewish people. I'd like to go up to them and say, 'I love you.' I'd like to kiss them.

There was another Jewish man in the library. He used to be in my class. In the Frogner school. He's from England. His face is also somehow painful. A finely curved nose, a delicate mouth, deep eyes. He looks so young, as if he'd just turned eighteen, and so Jewish, so fine looking, so painfully fine looking. I used to see him at school a lot. Once he said 'Cheer up!' to me. And to his brother, 'She is always so sad.' I'd really love to have kissed him today, but he just gave me a fleeting glance.

Those are the men in my life. Then, of course, there's the old man I model for. I'm just waiting for my love to be consecrated. He's so short and has a hunchback. He's the first man who has seen me naked. Today I passed out. When I leave him I always feel as if I'm parting from a friend; there's something that binds us. I'd love to know what's hiding behind his face. We speak very little.

'Is it cold?'

'How dark it is today!'

'Hold your right arm a little further to the left.'

Sunday, 23 November 1941, Lillestrøm

It's totally unjust not to have a home. It's totally unjust to have to take a mean comment from Frau Strøm.

Monday, 1 December 1941, Lillestrøm

It's very interesting working as a model. You have contact with so-called artists. You learn things: ah, so these are the select individuals who produce works of art. But very often these 'works of art' turn out to be anything but art.

Esval, the short, hunchbacked man, is very sweet. I think that deep down he is a very good man. He has a haggard, wizened face. And yet there's something childish in his eyes and his smile.

He draws me with a pencil on ordinary newsprint. Sometimes he captures a position excellently. But no individual perception, no individual *style* ever emerges in his drawings. His pictures that hang on the wall are very poor. Not art. But he's sweet. Today he gave me five kroner extra and said with his sweet smile, 'I've sold such a lot.' That was nice. Not just because of the five kroner.

Another painter drew me recently. I believe his name is Refsum. He drew me and then coloured in the drawing superbly. Once I had one arm over my breasts, the other hanging down limply. His drawing was wonderful. Perhaps wonderful is an exaggeration. To put it better, there was an individual *charm* about his drawings, especially in the colours. Today I sat for three women. Two 'painted' appallingly. On canvas. One of them used completely lifeless colours (Jensen) and made serious mistakes in her composition. The other one's composition (Nordahl-Lund) was even more inaccurate and she kept on coming out with profound comments, especially about art. The third one (Refsum) painted the human figure fairly well. It was lovely to listen to them talk about their work. Another thought I had was: I imagine it won't be long before I'm fed up with the so-called artist's crisis.

1. A few days ago five more Norwegians were shot: sabotage.

2. Politics is now mixing with the food issue: unwilling and lazy people don't get as much as hard-working individuals, etc.

3. Rostov was evacuated by the Germans.

4. The Norwegians are continuing to hold out. I love them. They are a brave people. They won't be forced to support the NS†.

† National Socialists; Nazis.

From *Ruth Maier's Diary*, edited by **Jan Erik Vold** and translated from the German by Jamie Bulloch (Harvill Secker 2009)

Ruth Maier was born into a middle-class Jewish family in interwar Vienna. Following the *Anschluss* of Austria in 1938, her sister having left for England, Ruth emigrated to Norway. Norway itself became a Nazi conquest in April 1940, and Ruth's attempts to join her family in Britain became urgent. Then, eleven months after the the entries quoted, in November 1942 she was deported by ship and train to Auschwitz. Of her last journey it is known that 188 women, 42 children and 116 men unfit for work were taken to the gas chambers immediately on their arrival. No death certificate exists for any of these 346 individuals.

    Ruth Maier kept a diary from 1934 until just before she was murdered at the age of twenty-two. It is politically mature, emotionally candid about herself and perceptive about others, and an intensely moving indication of the remarkable writer she was never allowed to become.

Jamie Bulloch spent several years teaching German language and central European history at University College London, King's and Warwick University. He has also translated Paulus Hochgatterer's *The Sweetness of Life*.

Beaufort

Once, Lila asked me, what exactly was Beaufort? And I realized how difficult it is to describe. You have to have been there to understand, and even then that's not enough. Because Beaufort is a lot of things. Like any military outpost, Beaufort is backgammon, Turkish coffee and cheese toasts. You play backgammon for cheese toasts, whoever loses makes them for everyone – killer cheese toasts with pesto. When things are really boring, you play poker for cigarettes. Beaufort is living without a single second of privacy, long weeks with the squad, one bed pushed up against the next, the ability to pick out the smell from each man's boots in your sleep. With your eyes closed, and at any given moment, it's being able to name the guy who farted by the smell alone. This is how true friendship is measured. Beaufort is lying to your mother on the phone so she won't worry. You always say, 'Everything's fine, I've just had a shower and I'm going to bed,' when in fact you haven't showered for twenty-one days, the water in the tanks has been used up, and in a minute you're going up for guard duty. And not just guard duty, but guarding the scariest position there is. When she asks when you're coming home you answer in code. 'Mum, you know the name of the neighbour's dog? I get out of here on the day that begins with the same letter.' What's most important is to keep Hezbollah from listening in and working out when to bomb your convoy. You really want to tell her you love her, that you miss her, but you can't, because your entire squad is there. If you say that, you'll give them ammunition for months, they'll tear you apart with humiliation. And then there's the worst situation of all: in the middle of a conversation with your mother, the mortar shells start raining down on the outpost. She hears an explosion and then the line goes dead. She's over there shaking, certain her boy has been killed, she waits on the balcony for a visit from the army bereavement team. You can't stop thinking about her, feeling sorry for her, but it might be days before the phone line to the command post back in Israel can be reconnected. Worry. That was why I preferred not to call at all. I told my mother I'd been transferred to a base right on the border, near the fence, Lebanon-lite, not deep in at all – definitely not deep in Lebanon – so that she'd sleep at night. Gut feeling, you ask? She knew the truth the whole time, even if she didn't admit it till now.

Beaufort is the South Lebanon Army, the SLA, local Christians, a mad bunch of Phalangists. Cigarettes in their mouths all day long. Smelly, wild, funny. They come in every morning at eight o'clock and we put a guard on them. They build, renovate whatever's been destroyed by the air raids, do what they're told. They're not allowed inside the secure area, not even permitted near the dining room.

Beaufort is guard duty. Sixteen hours a day. How do you stay sane after thousands of dead hours? We're all fucked up in different ways, but do me a favour and don't choke it during guard duty. 'Choke it' is our way of saying 'jerk off'. And some of the boys choke it; they choke it big time. You won't believe this, but a lot of people get really turned on by our green jungle atmosphere. I'm not joking. Nature is romantic, sensual. You would lose control, too. And it's not only nature that turns us on. The Sayas Network, at 67 MHz, used for open transmissions between the outposts, can also give you a hard-on sometimes. It's not an official network – it got its underground nickname from a radio broadcaster who specializes in melancholy late night monologues – but everyone knows about it because everyone, overwhelmed by boredom at one time or another, tunes the dial to Sayas, the boys' favourite, where they can talk bullshit all night long and melt at the sound of the female voices. Because the girls from the command post are on the other end, back in the war room, hot as fire, no air-conditioning, no boys, no reason not to unbutton their shirts a little, let off some steam. They sprawl across their chairs – I'd bet on it – stretching, spreading their legs, dripping hormones, dying for someone to make them laugh, flirt with them, make a little date for when they're back in Israel. Why not? Give them what they really need. Sure, honey, I've got lots of weapons. I got my short-barrelled M-16 flat top, a real beauty. And my Glock, a fantastic pistol. And I also have... my personal weapon. Measure it? You want me to? No problem, sure, I'm happy to measure it for you... actually I've forgotten how long it is, apologies, honey. That's the way you talk, making it up as you go along, turning yourself on, and they giggle, toying and teasing on that very thin border, one step over the line, one step back, and you're dying to believe that maybe, at the end of the night, when all the other men have dropped out, the girls are left alone, poor things, stuck with having to satisfy one another. What, you don't think so? A little touching, great stuff, nobody's ever died of it. But don't get your hopes up: the sweeter her voice over the airwaves, the more of a dog she is. I take full responsibility for that statement, I've been disappointed often enough in my life. A high squeaky voice, on the other hand, means you might want to invest a little time, because she's got huge tits. That's a fact, I'm not messing you around.

Beaufort is going out on seventy-two-hour ambushes with a huge supply of beef jerky in your knapsack. You can't believe how much of that stuff you can eat in three days. Beef jerky with chocolate and beef jerky with strawberry jam. And how you can talk and talk without saying anything. Pretty soon you reach the point where you know everything about everyone. Who did what, when, with who, why, in what position and what he was thinking about while he was doing it. I can tell you about their parents, their brothers and sisters, their not-so-close friends, their darkest perversions. There's a lot of time alone, too, when you're fed up with all that talking. You think about yourself, your home. You wonder if your mother is hanging out the washing right now, or maybe she's watching Dudu Topaz on television. Lila's probably in the shower. I'm fantasizing. Or maybe she's cheating on me. Freezing cold – we call it 'cold enough for foxes' up here, ice cube cold, the nose is frozen and the extremities numb. The feet have been numb for ages. Fingers, too. That's Beaufort. You have chilblains all over but your belly is burning hot, dripping sweat even. At these times everyone starts thinking about some wanker drinking coffee on Sheinkin Street in Tel Aviv. And here I fucking am, smelling like diesel oil, sweating with fear, lying in the middle of nowhere, and nobody's going to help me if I die. It won't interest the bloke in that café on Sheinkin Street, when I'm blown to pieces a few minutes from now. He'll keep sipping from his mug, probably at the very moment it happens he'll tell a joke and everyone will pretend to laugh and then he'll go home and screw his girlfriend, he won't even turn on the news, and as far as he is concerned, nothing will have happened this evening. Because it really doesn't affect him: for him, it's business as usual. He drives to his desk job at army headquarters each morning in the car that Daddy bought him, finishes the army every afternoon at four o'clock, and drinks coffee with whipped cream all the time. Blond hair, five o'clock shadow, pretty ugly. Hate him? Of course, it helps sometimes. Hatred is an excellent antidote to boredom.

Beaufort is Oshri. He rolls over in my direction, lies next to me, chews my ear off in whispers. Every time. Just before darkness fades and we're almost done with an ambush, he has an attack. 'Tell me, Erez, please, man: how did I wind up here?' he asks. 'What am I doing here dressed up like a bush? Why do I paint my face? What am I, a child? Am I in a Crusader fortress, you fucking bastard? What is this, are we living in the Bible? Am I some sort of retard, pissing in bottles? What am I doing here in sub-zero temperatures, in the snow, waiting to knock off an Arab who decides to climb out of bed at three o'clock in the morning? Does this make sense to you? And then going back to that stinking rat hole I sleep in at the outpost?

Does that seem logical? Tell me, have you seen where I sleep? It isn't good for me here, really not good. Grown-ups shouldn't have to live like this, wallowing in black mud mixed with snow each night. It's a fucking nightmare. Too much of a nightmare for me. Open your eyes. People have been dying on this mountain for a thousand years, isn't it about time to give up? I swear, it doesn't make sense that Beaufort exists. I'm telling you, there's no such place and we're all stuck in this hell for no good reason. It's a mistake. All over the world you can phone wherever you want in seconds. I'm the only person who can't! Six minutes from here by air some sexy bitch is walking along the high street in a g-string, and her only worry is whether to buy the mandarin orange, ginger and green tea extract shampoo or the jasmine, rose and orchid extract one that's enriched with pure scented oils. 'For that extra shiny softness' my arse. Big fucking dilemma. God, give me that kind of dilemma any day.'

—

From *Beaufort* by **Ron Leshem**, translated from the Hebrew by Evan Fallenberg (Harvill Secker 2009)

Written as the diary of Liraz (Erez) Liberti, the head of a commando team stationed at the remote Crusader fortress of Beaufort during the Israeli occupation of Lebanon, *Beaufort* is a potent account not of a war but a retreat, a fight with no enemy, only an amorphous presence that fires missiles from the surrounding mountains. Ron Leshem's novel was hailed by critics and by the generation of soldiers who served in Lebanon, as the authentic voice of that period.

    Ron Leshem grew up near Tel Aviv. *Beaufort*, his first novel, won the Sapir Prize, Israel's top literary award, in 2006 as well as the Yitzhak Sadeh Prize for military literature.

Evan Fallenberg is a US-born writer and translator living in Israel. His novel *Light Fell* was awarded the American Library Association prize for fiction and the Edmund White Award, and his translation of Meir Shalev's *A Pigeon and a Boy* was a PEN Translation Prize finalist and winner of the National Jewish Book Award.

Al afia

One February night in 1995, Azel decided to abandon his sewing, convinced that Tangier was no longer a garment but one of those synthetic wool blankets brought back from Belgium by émigrés. The city was hidden beneath a fabric that trapped warmth without dispelling humidity. Tangier no longer had any shape, any centre; instead, it had lopsided public squares from which cars had dislodged the peasant women who once came from Fahs to sell their fruits and vegetables.

The city was changing, and its walls were cracking.

Azel stopped at the Whisky à Gogo, a bar run by a couple of Germans on the rue du Prince-Héritier. He hesitated an instant before pushing open the door. He was one of those men who believe everything that happens to them is written in the order of things, perhaps not in the great celestial Book, but written somewhere. What must happen, happens. He had very little freedom. He'd learned this at his mother's knee, yet he occasionally struggled against determinism through action, finding pleasure in changing his routines simply to defy the tyranny of fate. That night, pausing for a moment at the door, he had a presentiment, a sort of crazy desire to rush toward his destiny.

The place was strangely calm. A bleached blonde was serving the men drinking at the bar. One of the two German guys was at the cash register. He never smiled.

In the dark room, men were alone with their whiskey bottles. Everything was sinister and murky. Azel stopped short when he saw a stocky man drinking a lemonade at the bar. His back was turned, a back as wide as a flagstone, with a thick neck. Azel recognized him and thought, Mala pata! Bad luck: it was the caïd, the local gang leader, fearsome and powerful, a man of few words and no heart. People called him Al Afia, 'the fire'. A well-known passeur, he smuggled boatloads of illegal emigrants so determined to sneak across the straits – to 'burn up' the ocean – that they would set fire to their identification papers, hoping to avoid being sent home again if they were arrested.

Al Afia didn't burden himself with feelings. That man from the Rif Mountains had always been a smuggler. As a child, he'd accompanied his uncle on nights when boats arrived in Al-Hoceima to pick up merchandise. His job had been to keep watch, proudly handling the binoculars with expertise, like an army commander scanning the horizon. He'd hardly known his father, who had died in a truck accident. The uncle had taken the boy under his wing and made him a trusted lieutenant, so when this protector had disappeared in turn, Al Afia had naturally taken his place. He was the only one who understood how everything worked, knew the right people to see about a problem, had contacts in Europe whose phone numbers he'd memorised, remembered families who needed help because the father, uncle or brother was in prison. Al Afia was not afraid of anyone and cared only about his business. People said he knew so many secrets that he was a walking strongbox. This was the man at whom Azel, primed by a few beers, now began shouting, calling onlookers to witness.

'Look at that fat belly, a crook's belly, and that neck, it really shows how bad this man is – he buys everyone, of course, this country is one huge marketplace, wheeling and dealing day and night, everybody's for sale, all you need is a little power, something to cash in on, and it doesn't take much, just the price of a few bottles of whiskey, an evening with a whore, but for the big jobs, that can cost you, money changes hands, so if you want me to look the other way, let me know the time and place, no sweat, my brother, you want a signature, a little scribble at the bottom of the page, no problem, come see me, or if you're too busy, send your driver, the one-eyed guy, he won't notice a thing, and that's it, my friends, that's Morocco, where some folks slave like maniacs, working because they've decided to be honest, those fellows, they labour in the shadows, no one sees them, no one talks about them when in fact they should get medals, because the country functions thanks to their integrity, and then there are the others, swarming everywhere, in all the ministries, because in our beloved country, corruption is the very air we breathe, yes, we stink of corruption, it's on our faces, in our heads, buried in our hearts – in your hearts, anyway – and if you don't believe me, ask old Crook's Belly over there, old baldy, the armoured safe, the strongbox of secrets, the one sipping a lemonade because monsieur is a good Muslim, he doesn't drink alcohol, he goes often to Mecca, oh yes, he's a hajji – and I'm an astronaut! I'm in a rocket, I'm escaping into space, don't want to live any more on this earth, in this country, it's all fake, everyone's cutting some deal, well, I refuse to do that, I studied law in a nation that knows nothing of the Law even while it's pretending to demand respect for our laws, what a joke, here you have to respect the powerful, that's all, but for the rest, you're on your fucking own... As for you, Mohammed Oughali, you're nothing but a thief, a faggot – a zamel... an attaye...'

Azel was shouting louder and louder. One of the cops at the bar, outstandingly drunk, went over to whisper in Al Afia's ear: 'Leave him to me, we'll charge him with threatening our national security... securi-titty...'

Al Afia's thugs would obey his slightest signal, and he had to shut this little loudmouth up. He glanced at him. Two bruisers grabbed Azel and tossed him outside, punching him savagely.

'You're crazy, busting your ass to piss off the boss – anyone would think you wanted to wind up like your pal!'

Azel's first cousin, Noureddine, had been more than a friend – he'd been like a brother to him. Azel had hoped that one day his sister Kenza might marry Noureddine, but their cousin had drowned during a night crossing when Al Afia's men had overloaded a leaky tub. Twenty-four perished on an October night the Guardia Civil of Almería claimed was too stormy for any attempt at rescue.

Al Afia had flatly denied receiving any money – even though Azel had been right there when Noureddine had paid the smuggler twenty thousand dirhams. That man had more than one death on his conscience – but did he even have a conscience? His varied business interests were flourishing. He lived in a huge house in Ksar es-Seghir, on the Mediterranean coast, a kind of bunker where he piled up burlap bags stuffed with money. People said he had two wives, one Spanish, one Moroccan, who lived in the same house and whom no one had ever seen. Since kif trafficking wasn't enough for him, every two weeks he filled some old boats with poor bastards who gave him everything they had to get to Spain. Al Afia was never around on the nights the boats left; one of his men – a chauffeur, bodyguard, burglar, never the same guy – would supervise the operation. Al Afia had his snitches, his informers, and his cops as well. He called them 'my men'. Every so often, taking great care not to alert the police in Tangier, the authorities in Rabat would send soldiers to stop the boats and arrest the passeurs, and that's how a few of Al Afia's henchmen landed in jail. As long as they were imprisoned in Tangier, Al Afia looked after them as though they were his own children, making sure they had a daily meal, supporting their families. He had his connections in the local prison, where he knew the warden and above all the guards, whom he tipped even when none of his pals was in residence there.

He was a past master at corruption, expertly assessing every man's character, needs, weaknesses, neglecting no aspect of anyone's personality, and he had a finger in every pie. You'd have thought he had a doctorate in some outlandish science. Al Afia could read only numbers. For everything else, he had loyal and competent secretaries with whom he spoke a Riffian dialect of Berber and a few words of Spanish. Everyone considered him a generous man: 'wears his heart on his sleeve'; 'his house is yours'; 'the dwelling of Goodness'; and so on. To one man he would offer a trip to Mecca; to another, a plot of land, or a foreign car (stolen, obviously); to yet another, a gold watch, telling him, 'It's a little something nice for your wife.' He paid the medical expenses of his men and their families and night after night he offered drinks to everyone at the bar that had gradually become his headquarters.

Azel had studied law. After passing his baccalaureate exam with distinction, he'd received a state scholarship, but his parents couldn't pay the rest of his tuition. He'd been counting on his uncle, who practised law in the nearby town of Larache, to give him a job, but the uncle had had to close his office after some complicated business cost him most of his clientele. In fact, those clients had left him because he refused to do things the way everyone else did, which had earned him a bad reputation: 'Don't go to Maître El Ouali – he's an honest man, you can't make a deal with him, so he loses every case!' Azel had realized that his future was compromised, and that without some kind of pull he'd never find work. Many others were in the same boat, so he'd joined a sit-in of unemployed university graduates outside the Parliament in Rabat.

A month later, when nothing had changed, he decided to leave the country and headed back to Tangier on a bus. He even imagined an accident that would put an end to his life and his impossible predicament. He saw himself dead, mourned by his mother and sister, missed by his friends: a victim of unemployment, of a carelessly negligent system – such a bright boy, well educated, sensitive, warm-hearted, what a pity that he got on that damned bus with those bald tyres, driven by a diabetic who lost consciousness going around a curve... Poor Azel, he never had a chance to live, did everything he could to break free – just think, if he'd managed to set out for Spain, by now he'd be a brilliant lawyer or a university professor!

Azel rubbed his eyes. He went up to the bus driver and asked him if he had diabetes.

'Heaven forbid! Thank God, I'm as strong as a horse, and I place my life in God's hands. Why do you ask?'

'Just to know. The newspaper says that one in seven Moroccans has diabetes.'

'Forget it – you shouldn't believe what you read in the papers...'

From *Leaving Tangier* by **Tahar Ben Jelloun,** translated from the French by Linda Coverdale (Arcadia Books 2009)

Leaving Tangier deals with illegal immigration, this time from the perspective of Moroccans seeking work and a better life on the European mainland. *Le Monde* said that 'Of the thirty books Ben Jelloun has written, this is undoubtedly one of the most courageous.' A young man called Azel is intent upon leaving, one way or another, and at the brink of despair meets Miguel, a wealthy Spanish gallery-owner, who promises to take him to Barcelona if Azel will become his lover. When Azel agrees, a different kind of hell begins for the young Moroccan.

Tahar Ben Jelloun emigrated from Morocco to France in 1961. He is a novelist, essayist, critic, and poet, and his novels include *The Sacred Night,* which won the Prix Goncourt, Corruption, and *The Last Friend.* In 2004 Ben Jelloun won the International IMPAC Dublin Literary Award for *This Blinding Absence of Light.*

Linda Coverdale has translated more than fifty books, including Tahar Ben Jelloun's award-winning novel *This Blinding Absence of Light.* A Chevalier de l'Ordre des Arts et des Lettres, she won the 2006 Scott Moncrieff Prize and the 1997 and 2008 French-American Foundation Translation Prize.

Yalo

'Let's go, boys,' said the officer, and Yalo pulled back in terror and stuck his back against the wall, shivering with fear and cold. Two men came forward carrying a sack. The first was holding the opening of the sack, while the second had his hands underneath it.

'Come closer, come closer. Don't be frightened,' said the officer.

Yalo went rigid and stuck his backside even harder against the wall.

'I told you, don't be frightened,' said the officer. 'Come over here and take the sack from the boys and put it on.'

'How can I put it on?' asked Yalo in a low voice.

'Put your legs into it like it was a pair of trousers,' said the officer.

'Trousers?' asked Yalo softly, without taking in what was being asked of him, staying where he was because he didn't know what to do. He leaned his head against the wall and closed his eyes. The third man pounced on him, seized his shoulders and pulled him into the centre of the room. Then he went round behind him and put his arms round his chest, pressing up against him till he was joined to him in a total, form-fitting embrace. The two men with the sack now came forward and bent over while the third man lifted Yalo and forced him to put his legs into the sack. The first man then half raised Yalo's body and tied the sack round his waist.

The three men stood back, and Yalo was alone in the centre of the room. He felt something strange moving between his naked legs, but he only caught on to the game when the officer, a bamboo cane in his hand, came forward.

'Will you confess, or shall we begin?' asked the officer.

'I swear, I swear by Almighty God, I swear by Almighty God, I've confessed everything, but I'm yours. I've told you everything, but I'm ready to say whatever you want, whatever you like.'

'I think you're still bullshitting us,' said the officer.

'I told the truth. I swear, I swear, I am not, I am not bullshitting.'

The bamboo cane described an arc from the officer's hand and fell on the sack between Yalo's legs and the torture journey began. The cane stung what was in the sack to life, and the yowling and clawing and that awareness of the abyss began. The cane stung the animal a second time, and the cat began to lash out and twist in the space that separated the bottom of the sack from Yalo's crotch. A cat that quivered with savagery, that jumped and jumped, as though trying to climb Yalo's penis, gnawing and clawing. And it had whiskers. Yalo didn't see the whiskers yet he saw them. They gleamed in a kind of light. The cat's two eyes flashed in the darkness and its whiskers gleamed and Yalo fell to the ground. At first, his mind didn't take in what was happening. He heard scrabbling and yowling, but he only caught on when he heard the officer ordering the cane to make the cat jump up, and he understood that he was at the mercy of a savage cat.

'Kitty kitty, up up up,' said the officer.

So Yalo fell to the floor. Faced with the cat's attacks, he squatted down, and the animal's ferocity increased. It leapt and seized his testicles, and it was then that Yalo saw it and saw its whiskers and felt that his testicles were exploding and that his penis was dripping blood. He stood, in an attempt to get some help, but the officer's cane kept stinging the sack as he repeated 'Kitty kitty,' at which the cat would quiver and jump and jump and Yalo would fall.

Inside the sack, Yalo discovered how pain is eliminated in the face of fear, and how that valley which runs all the way to the depths of the earth had opened up in his belly.

The officer had the cane that whipped in his hand; Yalo had the sack that leapt at his crotch; the sack had the cat that gnawed and clawed and moaned and muttered. The cat's yowling was like the crying of a thousand babies, and Yalo was like a lonely baby who had lost its ability to scream.

And when Yalo put up his hands and his tears poured down, he confessed to everything.

'I'll confess now,' he wanted to say, but he didn't say. His voice came out like a hoarse yowling, and he fell, and he saw himself entering the forest of savage cats that gnawed at his limbs. He was like someone swimming; later he would say that he was like someone swimming in cats, and he named the sack the 'kitty pond' and he saw himself diving down into blood, clawing and yowling.

And he saw his tears.

For three days and three nights the tears fell and covered his eyes and his face, and he did not wipe them away. He left them to fall, take paths and make furrows, then drop onto his neck and cover his body.

In the end, the kitty pond baptized him in tears.

'The true baptism, my son, is the baptism of tears,' said his grandfather. 'I am now being baptised, so leave me. No, I am not upset. The tears fall of their own accord.'

From *Yalo* by **Elias Khoury**, translated from the Arabic by
Humphrey Davies (MacLehose Press 2009)

Yalo is the story of the interrogation and torture of Daniel Habeel Abyad, a
young man accused of raping women and robbing their lovers in a forest on
the edge of Beirut. From the outset, however, it is Daniel's *alter ego*, Yalo,
who asserts himself as the story's protagonist. Faced by the interrogator's
implacable demands for confessions, he responds by writing and rewriting
the story of his life, evolving from hapless victim to driven inquisitor of his
own history.

    Elias Khoury is the author of twelve novels, four volumes of literary
criticism and three plays. Khoury was the editor-in-chief of the cultural
supplement of Beirut's daily newspaper, *An-Nahar*, and is a Global
Distinguished Professor of Middle Eastern and Islamic Studies at
New York University.

Humphrey Davies has translated work by writers including Elias Khoury,
Bahaa Taher, Alaa Al Aswany, Muhammad Mustagab, Yusuf al-Shirbini,
Gamal al-Ghitani, Hamdy el-Gazzar, Khaled Al-Berry, and Ahmed Alaydi.
His translation of Khoury's *Gate of the Sun* was awarded the Banipal Prize
and that of Al Aswany's best-selling *The Yacoubian Building* was voted Best
Translation of 2007 by the Society of Authors.

See how much I love you

They ate candyfloss at the amusement park. They shot at silhouettes in the shooting gallery. They climbed into the bumper cars. They strolled like a couple of lovers from ride to ride. Santiago made suggestions, and Montse went along with them. On the rollercoaster they held each other so tight that their arms ached. They lost themselves in the crowd, trying to go unnoticed among the few tourists. She kept on talking nervously. 'I'd like to smoke,' she said. And Santiago ran to a tobacconist's to buy a packet of Chesterfields. Every time he had to pay for something he took out a roll of one-hundred-peseta notes which he wielded as if he were a bank teller. 'Now tell me, are you really rich?'

'Of course, richest man in the world, with you here.'

At noon Montse called home to tell the maid she was having lunch at Nuria's.

'Don't you have to call your parents?' she asked Santiago.

'Never. I don't owe them any explanations. I'm independent.'

'You're lucky!'

They ate at an expensive restaurant. Santiago tried hard to make Montse feel at ease. Later, when she opened the door to her building, with the books pressed to her, it seemed as though the world was spinning. She turned to say goodbye and felt him push her gently against the door. 'What are you doing?'

'What do you think?' They kissed. Montse felt a pair of hands reaching where no one had ever reached before. Her books fell to the floor with a thud. She had to make an effort to tear herself away. In spite of her tiredness she found it difficult to fall asleep. She thought she wouldn't brush her teeth, so as to keep Santiago's kiss in her mouth, but the taste of cigarettes was too strong. Daydreaming, she scribbled in her diary. In the morning she only hoped her family wouldn't find out.

Montse phoned her father early the next morning. She spoke to her sister Teresa and her mother as well. She told them she found the classes at the Academy boring and, lying, said she wanted to come to Cadaqués. At half past nine she was standing by the shoe shop, nervously holding her books. Santiago appeared in a white car, though not the convertible. Montse got in as if this were part of a daily routine, smiling, wanting to be near him. 'I don't believe for a second that you work in a bank, or that your father is the general manager.' The boy tensed up, stepped on the accelerator, and drove into the traffic. 'Santi, you're a liar. and I haven't lied to you at all.'

'Nor me, Montse, honest. I'm not a liar, I swear.' She realised she was putting him on the spot. She leaned back on the headrest and gently placed her hand on his leg.

'Tell me something, Santi. Have you loved many women?'

Santiago San Román smiled, trying to relax.

'No one as much as you, sweetheart.' Montse felt as though petals were raining down on her. Her ears tingled and her legs trembled.

'You're a liar,' she said, squeezing his leg, 'but I love it.'

'I swear I'm not lying to you. I swear on....' He trailed off. Judging from his face, a dark thought must have crossed his mind.

For a week Montse's books travelled in the back seat of a number of different cars. She had the feeling of seeing the world from above, of gliding over the city, only to put her feet back on the ground when she went back home. Every evening, before saying goodbye, Santiago would push her into the huge central shaft of the spiral staircase, and she would let him explore her body. They would kiss for hours, until their stomachs ached. Thousands of questions popped in her mind, but she didn't dare ask them for fear of breaking the spell. Santiago's background was obvious. He sounded like an outsider, behaved impulsively, contradicted himself. Although he tried to hide his hands, his broken, grease-stained nails looked more like a factory worker's than a banker's. But whenever Montse hinted at it he would squirm, and she didn't feel like giving him a hard time. Later, lying on her bed, she tried to take a step back and see things clearly. Every night she promised herself she would speak to Santiago the next time she saw him, but when it came to the crunch she was afraid of frightening him away.

Almost twenty-six years later, lying on that very bed, she was turning the same thoughts over in her mind. The pictures of Santiago in military uniform had sent her back in time. She seemed to have been looking into that gaze of his only a few hours ago as they had said goodbye huddled in the staircase shaft. She looked at her hands and felt old. Remembering these things was like digging up a dead person. She took out the picture she'd found in the hospital and placed it on the blanket, next to the other photographs. It was him, no doubt about it. She tried to recall her feelings when they told her that he had died. She could perfectly remember the faces of the tobacconist and her husband. Had it been Santiago's idea? Had he tried to take his revenge on her by faking his own death? Had it been some macabre joke or a rumour no one bothered to confirm? Montse's eyes stung from staring so hard at the pictures. She decided to go through with her plan, and took her mobile out of her bag. She looked up the number she'd quickly scribbled in her diary and dialled it. Her stomach was a bundle of nerves. It felt like lifting a tombstone to make sure the body was still there. She waited impatiently as the rings went on. Eventually someone picked up. It was a man's quiet voice.

'Mr Ayach Bachir?'

'Who is this?'

'My name is Dr Montserrat Cambra. May I speak to Mr Ayach Bachir?'

'It's me. I'm Ayach Bachir.'

'Oh, hello, I'm calling from Santa Creu hospital.'

'The hospital? What now?'

'Nothing, rest assured, nothing's happened. I just wanted to have a word about your wife.'

'My wife is dead. We buried her two days ago.'

'I know, Mr Bachir. I signed the death certificate.'

There was a silence at the other end of the line. Montse found it almost unbearably painful. She took a deep breath and continued.

'You see, I only wanted to tell you that, when they gave you back your wife's belongings, something was left behind in the hospital. It's a photograph. I'd like to give it back to you in person and have a word with you.'

'A photograph? What photograph?'

'One of the ones your wife was carrying in her bag.'

'They gave me those back.'

'I'm sorry to insist, but one of them was mislaid,' lied Montse, still firm. 'I know this is not a good moment, but if you don't mind I'd like to give it back to you. I can come to your house if you like.'

Again there was a pause.

'To my house? What did you say your name was?'

'Montserrat Cambra. I got your address from the hospital files. I've got your file right here,' she lied again. 'Carrer de Balboa. Is that correct?'

'Yes, that's where I live.'

'So if you don't mind...'

'I don't, that's very kind of you.'

Montse breathed out, relieved, as though she had just walked over quicksand.

'I'll come by tomorrow then, if that's convenient, of course.'

'It is convenient, yes. Any time. You'll be welcome.'

Montse hung up and put the phone in her bag. She tied the letters together with the red ribbon and returned them to their place. Her hand touched something inside the drawer. It was a blackened silver ring. She took it out and looked at it against the light, as though it were a prism. Her heart quickened once again, and she realised that a tear was rolling down her cheek and into the corner of her mouth.

—

From *See How Much I Love You* by **Luis Leante**, translated from the Spanish by Martin Schifino (Marion Boyars 2009)

When Montse and Santiago meet as teenagers in 1970s Barcelona, they have little idea where their romance will lead. As a conscript in the Spanish army, Santiago spends his military service in the Western Sahara, Spain's only African colony, and is one of the few soldiers to befriend the local Saharawi people. But the year is 1975 and he is ensnared in the war between Saharawi and invading Moroccan forces.

See How Much I Love You, a love story spanning more than thirty years, was inspired by a humanitarian journey **Luis Leante** made to the Western Sahara, when he saw the reality of the Saharawis' refugee status, living in desert conditions more than thirty years after the Moroccan invasion. Luis Leante teaches classics in a high school at Alicante and has written six novels and two novels for children. *See How Much I Love You* won the 2007 Alfaguara prize for fiction.

Martin Schifino studied Comparative Literature at the University of Buenos Aires and for an MA in Medieval English at King's College, London. He works as a reviewer for the *Times Literary Supplement* and as a literary translator.

The reality and the record

Everyone staying at the refugee reception centre has two stories – the real one and the one for the record. The stories for the record are the ones the new refugees tell to obtain the right to humanitarian asylum, written down in the immigration department and preserved in their private files. The real stories remain locked in the hearts of the refugees, for them to mull over in complete secrecy. That's not to say it's easy to tell the two stories apart. They merge and it becomes impossible to distinguish them. Two days ago a new Iraqi refugee arrived in Malmö in southern Sweden. They took him to the reception centre and did some medical tests on him. Then they gave him a room, a bed, a towel, a bedsheet, a bar of soap, a knife, fork and spoon, and a cooking pot. Today the man is sitting in front of the immigration officer telling his story at amazing speed, while the immigration officer asks him to slow down as much as possible.

They told me they had sold me to another group and they were very cheerful. They stayed up all night drinking whiskey and laughing. They even invited me to join them in a drink but I declined and told them I was a religious man. They bought me new clothes, and that night they cooked me a chicken and served me fruit and sweets. It seems I fetched a good price. The leader of the group even shed real tears when he said goodbye. He embraced me like a brother.

'You're a very good man. I wish you all the best, and good luck in your life,' said the man with one eye.

I think I stayed with the first group just three months. They had kidnapped me on that cold accursed night. That was in the early winter of 2006. We had orders to go to the Tigris and it was the first time we had received instructions directly from the head of the Emergency Department in the hospital. At the bank of the river the policemen were standing around six headless bodies. The heads had been put in an empty flour sack in front of the bodies. The police guessed they were the bodies of some clerics. We had arrived late because of the heavy rain. The police piled the bodies onto the ambulance driven by my colleague Abu Salim and I carried the sack of heads to my ambulance. The streets were empty and the only sounds to break the forlorn silence of the Baghdad night were some gunshots in the distance and the noise of an American helicopter patrolling over the Green

Zone. We set off along Abu Nawas Street towards Rashid Street, driving at medium speed because of the rain. I remembered the words the director of the Emergency Department in the hospital often used to say: 'When you're carrying an injured person or a patient close to death, the speed of the ambulance shows how humane and responsible you are.' But when you are carrying severed heads in an ambulance, you needn't go faster than a hearse drawn by mules in a dark medieval forest. The director saw himself as a philosopher and an artist, but 'born in the wrong country,' as he would say. He took his work seriously nonetheless and considered it a sacred duty, because to him running the ambulance section of the Emergency Department meant managing the dividing line between life and death. We called him the Professor and my other colleagues hated him and called him mad. I know why they hated him, because the enigmatic and aggressive way he spoke made him seem screwed up in the eyes of others. But I retained much respect and affection for him because of the beautiful and fascinating things he said. Once he said to me: 'Spilt blood and superstition are the basis of the world. Man is not the only creature who kills for bread, or love, or power, because animals in the jungle do that in various ways, but he is the only creature who kills because of faith.' He would usually wrap up his speeches by pointing to the sky and declaiming theatrically: 'The question of humanity can be solved only by constant dread.' My colleague Abu Salim had a notion that the Professor had links with the terrorist groups because of the violent language he used, but I would loyally defend the man, because they did not understand that he was a philosopher who refused to make foolish jokes, as the stupid ambulance drivers did all day. I remembered every sentence and every word he said, for I was captivated by my affection and admiration for him.

Let me get back to that wretched night. When we turned towards the Martyrs Bridge I noticed that the ambulance driven by Abu Salim had disappeared. Then in the side mirror I caught sight of a police car gaining on us at high speed. I pulled over to the side in the middle of the bridge. Four young men in masks and special police uniforms got out of the police car. The leader of the group pointed his pistol in my face and told me to get out of the vehicle, while his colleagues unloaded the sack of heads from the ambulance.

'I've been kidnapped and they are going to cut off my head.' That was my first thought when they tied me up and stuffed me in the boot of the police car. It took me only ten minutes to realise what was awaiting me. I recited the Throne Verse from the Quran three times in the darkness of the boot and I felt that my skin was starting to peel off. For some reason in those dark moments I thought about my body weight, maybe 70 kilos. The slower the car went, or the more it turned, the more frightened I was, and when it picked up speed again a strange blend of tranquility and anxiety would pulse through me. Perhaps I thought at those moments of what the Professor had said about the correlation between speed and the imminence of death. I didn't understand exactly what he meant, but he would say that someone about to die in the forest would be more afraid than someone about to die in a speeding ambulance, because the first one feels that fate has singled him out, while the second imagines there are others sticking with him. I also remember that he once announced with a smile: 'I would like to have my death in a spaceship travelling at the speed of light.'

I imagined that all the unidentified and mutilated bodies I had carried in the ambulance since the fall of Baghdad lay before me, and that in the darkness surrounding me I then saw the Professor picking my severed head from a pile of rubbish, while my colleagues made dirty jokes about my liking for the Professor. I don't think the police car drove very far before it came to a halt. At least they did not leave the city. I tried to remember the Rahman Verse of the Quran but they got me out of the car and escorted me into a house which smelt of grilled fish. I could hear a child crying. They undid my blindfold and I found myself in a cold, unfurnished room. Then three madmen laid into me and beat me to a pulp, until a darkness again descended.

I thought I heard a cock crow at first. I shut my eyes but I couldn't sleep. I felt a sharp pain in my left ear. With difficulty I turned over onto my back and pushed myself towards the window, which had recently been blocked up. I was very thirsty. It was easy to work out that I was in a house in one of Baghdad's old neighbourhoods. In fact I don't know exactly what details of my story matter to you, for me to get the right of asylum in your country. I find it very hard to describe those days of terror, but I want to mention also some of the things which matter to me. I felt that God, and behind him the Professor, would never abandon me throughout my ordeal. I felt the presence of God intensely in my heart, nurturing my peace of mind and calling me to patience. The Professor kept my mind busy and alleviated the loneliness of my captivity. He was my solace and my comfort. Throughout those arduous months I would recall what the Professor had said about his friend, Dawoud the engineer. What did he mean by saying that the world is all interconnected? And where do the power and the will of God stand in such matters? We were drinking tea at the hospital door when the Professor said: 'While my friend Dawoud was driving the family car through the streets of Baghdad, an Iraqi poet in London was writing a fiery article in praise of the resistance, with a bottle of whiskey on the table in front of him to help harden his heart. Because the world is all interconnected, through feelings, words, nightmares, and other secret channels, out of the poet's article jumped three masked men. They stopped the family car and killed Dawoud, his wife, his child and his father. His mother was waiting for them at home. Dawoud's mother doesn't know the Iraqi poet nor the masked men. She knows how to cook the fish which was awaiting them. The Iraqi poet fell asleep on the sofa in London in a drunken stupor, while Dawoud's mother's fish went cold and the sun set in Baghdad.'

The wooden door of the room opened and a young man, tall with a pale and haggard face, came in carrying breakfast. He smiled at me as he put the food down in front of me. At first I was uncertain what I could say or do. But then I threw myself at his feet and implored him tearfully: 'I am the father of three children... I'm a religious man who fears God... I have nothing to do with politics or religious denominations... God protect you... I'm just an ambulance driver... before the invasion, and since the invasion... I swear by God and his noble Prophet.' The young man put a finger to his lips and rushed out. I felt that my end had come. I drank the cup of tea and performed my prayers in the hope that God would forgive my sins. At the second prostration I felt that a layer of ice was forming across my body and I almost cried out in fear, but the young man opened the door, carrying a small lighting device attached to a stand, and accompanied by a boy carrying a Kalashnikov rifle. The boy stood next to me, pointing the gun at my head, and from then on he did not leave his place. A fat man in his forties came in, taking no notice of me. On the wall he hung a black cloth banner inscribed with a Quranic verse urging Muslims to fight jihad. Then a masked man came in with a video camera and a small computer. Then a boy came in with a small wooden table. The masked man joked with the boy, tweaked his nose and thanked him, then put the computer on the table and busied himself with setting up the camera in front of the black banner. The thin young man tried out the lighting system three times and then left.

'Abu Jihad, Abu Jihad,' the fat man shouted.

The young man's voice came from outside the room: 'Wait a minute. Right you are, Abu Arkan.'

This time the young man came back carrying the sack of heads which they had taken from the ambulance. Everyone blocked their nose because of the stink from the sack. The fat man asked me to sit in front of the black banner. I felt that my legs were paralysed, but the fat man pulled me roughly by my shirt collar. At that point another man came in, thick-set with one eye, and ordered the fat man to let me be. This man had in his hand an army uniform. The man with one eye sat close to me, with his arm across my shoulders like a friend, and asked me to calm down. He told me they wouldn't slaughter me if I was cooperative and kind-hearted. I didn't understand fully what he meant by this 'kind-hearted'. He told me it would only take a few minutes. The one-eyed man took a small piece of paper from his pocket and asked me to read it. Meanwhile the fat man was taking the decomposing heads out of the sack and lining them up in front of me. It said on the piece of paper that I was an officer in the Iraqi army and these were the heads of other officers, and that accompanied by my fellow officers I had raided houses, raped women and tortured innocent civilians, that we had received orders to kill from a senior officer in the US Army, in return for large financial rewards. The man with one eye asked me to put on the army uniform and the cameraman asked everyone to pull back behind the camera. Then he came up to me and started adjusting my head, as a hairdresser does. After that he adjusted the line of heads, then went back behind the camera and called out: 'Off you go.'

The cameraman's voice was very familiar. Perhaps it resembled the voice of a famous actor, or it might have been like the voice of the Professor when he was making an exaggerated effort to talk softly. After they filmed the videotape, I didn't meet the members of the group again, other than the young man who brought me food, and he prevented me from asking any questions. Every time he brought food he would tell me a new joke about politicians and men of religion. My only wish was that he would let me contact my wife, because I had hidden some money for a rainy day in a place where even the jinn would never think of looking, but they vehemently rejected my request. The one-eyed leader of the group told me that everything depended on the success of the videotape, and in fact the tape was such a success so quickly that everyone was surprised. Al Jazeera broadcast the videotape. They allowed me to watch television and on that day they were jumping for joy, so much so that the fat man kissed me on the head and said I was a great actor. What made me angry was the Al Jazeera newsreader, who assured viewers that the channel had established through reliable sources that the tape was authentic and that the Ministry of Defence had admitted that the officers had gone missing. After the success of the broadcast they started treating me in a manner which was better than good. They took trouble over my food and bedding and allowed me to have a bath.

Their kindness culminated on the night they sold me to the second group. Then three masked men from that group came into the room and, after the man with one eye had given me a warm farewell, the new men laid into me with their fists, tied me up and gagged me, then shoved me into the boot of a car which drove off at terrifying speed.

—

From *The Madman of Freedom Square* by **Hassan Blasim**, translated from the Arabic by Jonathan Wright (Comma Press 2009)

Hassan Blasim's stories present an uncompromising view of the West's relationship with Iraq, taking in events from the Iran-Iraq war through to the occupation. He blends allegory with historical realism and confounds readers' expectations by a comedy of the macabre that makes the stories both fantastic and shockingly real. This collection represents the first literary work about these times from an Iraqi perspective.

Hassan Blasim is a poet, film-maker and short story writer. He studied at the city's Academy of Cinematic Arts and in 1998 left Baghdad for Iraqi Kurdistan, where he continued to make films under a pseudonym, fearing for the safety of his family in Baghdad. In 2004, he moved to Finland, where he has since made numerous short films and documentaries for Finnish television. *The Madman of Freedom Square* is his first book.

Jonathan Wright studied Arabic at Oxford University in the 1970s and has spent much of the past three decades in the Arab world, mostly as a journalist. He has also translated Khaled el-Khamissi's best-selling fictional monologues, *Taxi*.

The book of the street

Fourth floor, I buzz the entryphone and hear what sounds like squealing, oohs and aahs.

This must be it. I boldly step into the filthy lobby.

Patricia and Lucretia are already old men; whatever lives they once enjoyed are long over and done with. Since 1992, to be precise. Patricia: a heavy-set, run-down man with a huge bald patch and animated, bushy eyebrows. Lucretia: wrong side of fifty, smooth-shaven, cynical, just as fat. Black fingernails eaten away by ringworm, little jokes, blasé airs, stock phrases: 'If they finish school, they're not real men!' Their whole lives they made ends meet working as hostesses, orderlies, cloakroom attendants. It was a way to get by while giving themselves time for the really important things.

I take a rickety lift up to the fourth floor of a gloomy, socialist apartment block, circa 1960. Stinks of piss. Out in the courtyard little kids are screaming their heads off. I look at the buttons scorched here and there by cigarettes, labels peeling. I read the graffiti: football slogans, a threat to send someone to the ovens. I give the bell a quick poke. The door opens immediately; it's Lucretia. Patricia is in the kitchen, making the tea. They're both excited about the 'reporter man' who's come to visit; they're acting like real celebrities. For now they're living off their pensions, barely scraping by. They don't even have a vegetable patch where they can grow a few cloves of garlic, or share memories of the good old days over the garden fence with the old dear next door. No, their memories aren't things you'd want strangers to hear. Which is exactly why I'm going to hear them today.

Lucretia had once been a German teacher, but he could never keep a job for long; he was always landing himself in trouble by making the moves on his students, until finally he ended up working as a private tutor. In the seventies, he moved from Bydgoszcz to Wrocław. Here, in a park where the queers go, in a dirty public toilet, he met Patricia. Patricia was sprawled out, drunk, his head in a pool of piss, thinking he'd never get back on his feet. But Lucretia helped the little slut out, finding him a job as a cloakroom attendant in a workers' cultural centre. From then on, it was Patricia's job to dispense ping-pong balls to young functionaries who came to play table tennis in the club room. The work was easy, the pay like any other. By day, Patricia drank coffee out of recycled mustard jars and gossiped with the caretaker. Night was when she came alive. Sometimes she stayed out on her shift, as if she were a night porter, until dawn. Then she would fantasise that she was a Baroque lady wearing an enormous crinoline and a tall wig, taking a carriage to see her lover; she imagined she had some completely unpronounceable name and a huge fan to hide her face behind. The roof might be leaking into a bucket, the wind howling outside the window, but Patricia would get up, make coffee or tea with a little heating coil, add a shot of vodka, then return to her carriage, to Versailles, to skirts so wide you could fit a couple of lovers and a bottle of poison under their pleats. She'd light up a Wiarus and go on her rounds, and by the time she returned she had already worked out her next step. All she needed were earplugs, because the nights were never quiet, and the guard dogs outside were always chasing cats. Morning sobered her up like a splash of cold water. She had to clock off, she had to go back; once again people would be making demands of her, and once again she would be lazy and insubordinate in return.

But that was a long time ago, back when the workers at Hydral and Stolbud still had energy at the end of the working day for things like ballet, back before phrases like 'child molesting' had been invented, and newspapers were only interested in their own problems. Television had yet to come to the night shift, so people had to let their imaginations run at full steam, else they would die of boredom.

Today the rooms in Patricia's cultural centre have all been taken over by different companies. The façade is plastered with signs showing which floor houses the pawn shop, the currency exchange, the pool hall, the candle wholesaler. What was once a studio where workers awkwardly learned to dance now has the romantic moniker 'Everything for Five Zlotys'. Nobody wants to give Patricia a job any more, everyone's just looking out for number one, and building security is handled by a special firm. The world is a bad place because the poetry recitation contests, the girls' calisthenics, the ballet classes, and the corrective gymnastics have given way to filthy dens where wannabe-mafiosi trade unfashionable second-hand mobile phones. And as if that wasn't bad enough, you can't buy earplugs at the kiosks any more. Patricia gave this all some thought and decided, with no regrets, to take her much-deserved pension.

Poland's Third Republic never got a foot in her door.

They refer to each other as *she* and *her*, call each other *sister* or *girl*, and it wasn't all that long ago that they were still picking up men – in the park, behind the opera house, and at the train station. Who knows how much is true, how much is legend, and how much is simply taking the piss. But one thing is sure: they're just two of the innumerable legion of sex addicts. Connoisseurs of cock! Even today, pot-bellied pensioners, they have a few tricks up their sleeves. Neither has ever heard of plastic surgery or sex-change operations. They get by with a flourish or two of their plain black satchels, which they call 'handbags'. They make do with what they've got – the quintessence of communist-era mediocrity. All they have to do is hold their cigarettes a little differently, shave every day, and put their words, their language, to use. For their power lies in their words. They have nothing; whatever they do have they've had to make up, lie up, sing up. Today you can buy anything you want: your sex, your eye colour, your hair – there's no place left for the imagination. Which is why they would rather be poor and 'have a bit of fun'.

'Oh *stop*, darling!' Patricia gets 'dramatic' and pours tea into a chipped cup; old and grimy though it may be, it still comes on a saucer and with a serviette. Form, form is all that matters. And words.

'Oh stop! My glory days are long over, my arse is even sagging. O where o where are the snows of yesteryear? Christ, what a fruity-pie! what a crazy dame! Do you mind? Old Villon said it best: it's better to choose boys. And boy could we choose 'em!'

Being 'dramatic', 'camping it up', and 'being swish' mean acting like a woman, whatever they understand by that. Apparently it means flapping their hands and squealing, saying things like 'Oh stop!' and 'Christ, Christina!', or going up to a cute lad, holding their bent wrists in his face, and saying, 'Sit up straight, puppy dog, when you're talking to me!'

They don't want to be women at all; they want to be swishy men. That's how they like it, how they've been their whole lives: pretend femmes. To actually be a woman would be beside the point. What's exciting is the pretending; to actually satisfy their imagination would be... but satisfaction isn't a word in their language. The only words they know are 'hunger', 'frustration', 'cold night', 'wind', and 'come with me'. A permanent stopover in the upper regions of the depths, between the railway station, where the pickings were slimmest, their miserable jobs and the park, where the public toilet was. The arsehole of the world.

And as it happens, someone had lined this arsehole with sawdust and rags especially for them. All comfy and cosy.

No one ever went hungry with that tinned soup, with those potatoes, the subsidies of socialism. There was always enough to eat and a roof over your head; a lady doesn't need much to get by. Now they're building a great big shopping mall in that park of theirs; they're burying their entire history. Patricia insists she will protest. But she's only kidding. More bitterly and sadly every time. 'What can a bag lady like me do? Lay into Big Capital with my walking stick? Hit it over the head with my handbag? What should I tell them, that it's an historic site? Oh, go and get the ashtray, Lucretia, the gentleman has nowhere to put his (ha! ha!) *aaaassshh!*'

Patricia realises she's called herself a 'bag lady', and she's delighted at her new joke. Somewhere deep down it contains a trickle of indignity, and Patricia is already planning to drink it, to lick it up like a drop of eggnog from the bottom of a glass. Tonight.

'So there I am on my way to the park. First I stop at the kiosk and buy some cigarettes, like I've done for years. They're fine; they're not at all seriously harmful to my health. Then I see this guy I knew way back, made a name for himself, a businessman. and he cuts me this look like I'm a prostitute or something, like I'm a streetwalker down by the station. Well, I suppose I am walking the street. But I'm nobody's streetwalker... so I listen to what he says, but none of it has anything to do with me, something about the credit. Can you believe it? He's got the credit, but he's losing his job. And I'm thinking, darling, if all I needed was credit to make me happy... so I'm having all these deep philosophical thoughts, see, and Lucia La Douche, who I share them with, completely agrees. That we're living in the highest regions of the depths, like in paradise. Nothing can threaten us, and...' – Lucretia lazily stretches her entire body – 'life actually has meaning!' She licks herself indecently.

I'm sitting at the wobbly table in the kitchen of their dilapidated flat. Nothing has changed here since the days of communism. All around me are Taiwanese gold watches from the market, barometers from the market, glittery figurines from the market, all of it from Russia. Even their speech is full of Russianisms:

'Not much by him in the trousers....'

Grinding poverty. Their laundry dries on a line hung over the stove. Men's underwear, all of it black, and the cheapest brand; darned socks, black too. First, because black is weird, and second, because mourning is the rule in this household, and has been for over a decade.

Lucretia poses like a dowager countess deprived of her fortune by the vicissitudes of war. She crosses her legs (a pale calf, tattooed with a web of veins, appears between her sock and the cuff of her brown trousers), lights a cigarette, holds the smoke in for a moment, then releases it with a deep sigh, a lady lost in revery. They put on their favourite Anna German record. The disc spins round on the turntable:

In the café on the corner there's a concert every night
Stay there in the doorway, you dancing Eurydices,
Before the walls are streaked with the day's first light
May your drunken Orpheuses
Hold you in their arms...

They offer me a cup of sweet, lukewarm tea. Their flat is furnished like the waiting room of a clinic. You can tell how little people need in life when they 'live' by other means, when their flat is nothing more than a waiting room, somewhere to spend the time between nocturnal forays. It's seedy, as the homes of (sex) addicts usually are. The bottom halves of the walls are painted with a yellow, oil-based paint; the top halves are grimy. The windowsills are lined with white plastic pots of grasses and a recently deceased money tree. I wait for the two ladies (gentlemen?) to finally sit down for their tea and cigarettes, to stop running around. But the moment one takes a seat, the other suddenly realises she needs to spray her armpits with deodorant, or brush her hair in front of the cracked mirror. Something is cooking in the kitchen, too, and Lucretia gets up to water the plants from a communist-era milk bottle. Who knows where that came from? They preen and primp themselves the whole time. Guests make rare appearances in this house of mourning.

'Let's begin. First, perhaps you could tell me something about life for homosexuals in Wrocław back then?'

From *Lovetown* by **Michał Witkowski**, translated from the Polish by
W. Martin (Portobello Books 2010)

Growing up queer in a communist state, Patricia and Lucretia spent the
1970s and 1980s underground, finding glamour in the squalor, in parks and
public toilets, seducing hard Soviet soldiers, preying on drunks and seeing
their friends die of AIDS. Their life was constrained, but when they hit
Lovetown, populated by a younger and flashier generation who are out and
proud in their post-communist paradise, they make the discovery that where
anything goes, some things have also been lost.

    Michał Witkowski was born in 1975 in Wrocław. He has written a
doctoral dissertation in Polish philology at the University of Wrocław and
published five books, two of which were nominated for Poland's prestigious
NIKE Literary Award. *Lovetown*, which also won the Polish Booksellers
Association Prize, has been published in 16 languages.

W. Martin has published translations of work by Natasza Goerke, Marcin
Świetlicki, Erich Kästner and Günter Grass. He edited the 'New Polish
Writing' issue of the *Chicago Review* and is the recipient of a 2008 NEA
Fellowship in translation. He currently works for the Polish Cultural
Institute in New York.

Somewhere in Afghanistan or elsewhere

The hurricane lamp breathes its final breaths in vain. The flame goes out. The woman returns. She is filled with a deep weariness – of her being, and her body. After a few listless steps towards her man, she stops. Less decisive than the previous day. Her gaze lingers desperately on the motionless body. She sits down between the man and the Koran, which she opens at the flyleaf. She moves her finger over the names of God, one by one. Counts them. Stops at the seventeenth name. Murmurs '*Al-Wahhab*, the Bestower'. A bitter smile puckers the edges of her lips. 'I don't need a gift.' She pulls at the peacock feather peeking out of the Koran. 'I haven't the heart to go on reciting the names of God.' She strokes her lips with the feather. 'Praise be to God… He will save you. Without me. Without my prayers… he's got to.'

The woman is silenced by a knocking at the door. 'It must be the Mullah.' She hasn't the slightest desire to open. More knocking. She hesitates. The knocking continues. She leaves the room. Her footsteps can be heard moving towards the road. She is talking to someone. Her words are lost in the courtyard, behind the windows.

A hand timidly pushes open the door to the room. One of the little girls comes in. A sweet face beneath a mop of unruly hair. She is slender. Her little eyes stare at the man. 'Daddy!' she cries, and shyly walks closer. 'Are you sleeping, Daddy?' she asks. 'What's that in your mouth?' pointing at the drip tube. She stops near her father, unsure whether to touch his cheek. 'But you're not sleeping!' she cries. 'Why does Mummy always say you're sleeping? Mummy says you're sick. She won't let me come in here and talk to you… but she's always talking to you.' She is about to sit down next to him when she is stopped by a cry from her sister, squeezed into the half-open doorway. 'Be quiet!' she shouts, mimicking her mother's voice, and runs up to the little one. 'Come on!' She takes her by the hand and pulls her towards their father. After a moment's hesitation, the younger girl climbs on to her father's chest and starts yanking at his beard. The other shouts heartily, 'Come on, Daddy, talk!' She leans towards his mouth and touches the tube. 'Take out this thing. Talk!' She pulls away the tube, hoping to hear him say something. But no. Nothing but breathing. Slow, deep breaths. She stares at her father's half-open mouth. Her curious little hand dives in and pulls out the fly. 'A fly!' she cries and, disgusted, throws it on the floor. The younger girl laughs, and rests her chapped cheek on her father's chest.

The mother comes in. 'What are you doing?' she screams in horror. She rushes towards the children, grabbing them by the arms. 'Get out! Come with me!' 'A fly! Daddy's eating a fly!' shriek the girls, almost in concert. 'Be quiet!' orders their mother.

They leave the room.

The fly struggles on the kilim, drowning in saliva.

The woman comes back into the room. Before reinserting the tube into the man's mouth she looks around, anxious and intrigued. 'What fly?' Noticing nothing, she replaces the tube and leaves.

Later, she comes back to pour sugar-salt solution into the drip bag, and eye drops into the man's eyes.

Her tasks complete, she does not remain with her man.

She no longer puts her right hand on her man's chest.

She no longer tells the black prayer beads in time with her man's breathing.

She leaves.

She doesn't return until the call to midday prayer – and not to take out the little carpet, unfurl it, lay it on the ground and say her prayers. Just to put new eye drops into the man's eyes. One, two. One, two. And then leave again.

After the call to prayer, the Mullah's hoarse voice beseeches God to lend his protection to the area's faithful on this, a Wednesday: '... because, as our Prophet says, *it's a day of misfortune during which the Pharaoh and his people were drowned, and the peoples of the Prophet Salih – the Ad and the Thamoud – were destroyed...*' He stops and immediately starts again in a fearful voice. 'Dear Faithful, as I have always told you, Wednesday is a day on which, according to our Prophet, the most noble, *it is right neither to practise bloodletting, nor to give, nor to receive.* However, one of the hadith, quoted by Ibn Younes, says that this practice is permitted during Jihad. Today, your brother, our great Commander, is furnishing you with weapons that you may defend your honour, your blood, and your tribe!'

In the street, men are shouting themselves hoarse: '*Allah O Akbar!*' Running: '*Allah O Akbar!*' Their voices fading as they near the mosque: '*Allah O...*'

A few ants prowl around the corpse of the fly on the kilim. Then grab hold of it and carry it off.

The woman arrives to gaze anxiously at the man. Perhaps she is afraid that the call to arms will have put him back on his feet.

She stays near the door. Her fingers stroke her lips and then, nervously, stray between her teeth, as if to extract words that don't dare express themselves. She leaves the room. She can be heard making something for lunch, talking and playing with the children.

Then it's time for a nap.

Darkness.

Silence.

The woman comes back. Less anxious. She sits down next to the man. 'That was the Mullah. He was here for our prayer session. I told him that since yesterday I have been impure, that I am menstruating, like Eve. He wasn't happy. I'm not sure why. Because I dared compare myself to Eve, or because I told him I was bleeding? He left, muttering into his beard. He wasn't like that before; you could have a joke with him. But since you people declared this new law for the country, he's changed too. He's afraid, poor man.'

Her gaze settles on the Koran. Suddenly, she jumps: 'Shit, the feather!' She looks for it inside the book. Not there. Under the pillow. Not there either. In her pockets. There it is. With a big sigh, she sits down. 'That Mullah is driving me out of my mind!' she says as she puts the feather back inside the Koran. 'What was I talking about?... Oh yes, bleeding... I was lying to him, of course.' She glances keenly at the man, more mischievous than submissive. 'Just as I've lied to you... more than once!' She pulls her legs up to her chest and wedges her chin between her knees. 'But there is something I'd better tell you....' She looks at him for a long time. Still with the same strange wariness in her gaze. 'You know....' Her voice goes hoarse. She swallows to moisten her throat, and looks up. 'When you and I went to bed for the first time – after three years of marriage, remember! – anyway, that night, I had my period.' Her gaze flees the man to seek refuge in the creases of the sheet. She rests her left cheek on her knees. The look in her scarred eye loses some of its wariness. 'I didn't tell you. And you, you thought that... the blood was proof of my virginity!' A muted laugh shakes her crouched, huddled body. 'How thrilled you were to see the blood, how proud!' A moment. A look. And the dread of hearing a cry of rage, an insult. Nothing. And so, soft and serene, she allows herself to visit the intimate corners of her memory. 'I shouldn't really have had my period then. It wasn't the right time, but I was a week early; it must have been nerves, fear about meeting you. I mean, can you imagine – being engaged for almost a year and then married for three years to an absent man; not so easy. I lived with your name. I had never seen or heard or touched you before that day. I was afraid, afraid of everything, of you, of going to bed, of the blood. But at the same time, it was a fear I enjoyed. You know, the kind of fear that doesn't separate you from your desire, but instead arouses you, gives you wings, even though it may burn.

That was the kind of fear I was feeling. And it was growing in me every day, invading my belly, my guts.... On the night before you arrived, it came pouring out. It wasn't a blue fear. No. It was a red fear, blood red. When I mentioned it to my aunt she advised me not to say anything... and so I kept quiet. That suited me fine. Although I was a virgin I was really scared. I kept wondering what would happen if by any chance I didn't bleed that night...' Her hand sweeps through the air as if batting away a fly. 'It would have been a catastrophe. I'd heard so many stories about that. I could imagine the whole thing.' Her voice becomes mocking. 'Passing off impure blood as virginal blood, bit of a brainwave, don't you think?' She lies down right close to the man. 'I have never understood why, for you men, pride is so much linked to blood.' Her hand sweeps the air again. Her fingers are moving. As if gesturing to an invisible person to come closer. 'And remember the night – it was when we were first living together – that you came home late. Dead drunk. You'd been smoking. I had fallen asleep. You pulled down my knickers without saying a word. I woke up. But I pretended to be deeply asleep. You... penetrated me ... you had a great time... but when you stood up to go and wash yourself, you noticed blood on your dick. You were furious. You came back and beat me, in the middle of the night, just because I hadn't warned you that I was bleeding. I had defiled you!' She laughs, scornful. 'I had made you unclean.' Her hand snatches memories from the air, closes around them, descends to stroke her belly as it swells and slackens at a pace faster than the man's breathing.

Suddenly, she thrusts her hand downwards, beneath her dress, between her legs. Closes her eyes. Takes a deep, ragged breath. Rams her fingers into herself, roughly, as if driving in a blade. Holding her breath, she pulls out her hand with a stifled cry. Opens her eyes and looks at the tips of her nails. They are wet. Wet with blood. Red with blood. She puts her hand in front of the man's vacant eyes. 'Look! That's my blood, too. Clean. What's the difference between menstrual blood and blood that is clean? What's so disgusting about this blood?' Her hand moves down to the man's nostrils. 'You were born of this blood! It is cleaner than the blood of your own body!' She pushes her fingers roughly into his beard. As she brushes his lips she feels his breath. A shiver of fear runs across her skin. Her arm shudders. She pulls her hand away, clenches her fist and, with her mouth against the pillow, cries out again. Just once. The cry is long. Heartrending. She doesn't move for a long time. A very long time. Until the water bearer knocks on the neighbour's door, and the old woman's rasping cough is heard through the walls, and the water bearer empties his skin into the neighbour's tank, and one of her daughters starts crying in the passage. Then, she stands up and leaves the room without daring to look at her man.

—

From **The Patience Stone** by **Atiq Rahimi**, translated from the French by Polly McLean (Chatto & Windus 2010)

In *The Patience Stone* a young woman sits at her husband's bedside, twisting her worry beads and reciting prayers. He is in a coma after being shot by a fellow soldier. Consumed by her vigil and his medical care, the woman is alone. Desperate for any sign of life, her mind begins to unravel, and as it does so becomes intensely clear-sighted. Now is her chance to speak without being censored… She pours out love and hate, sexual desires and hopes, as though to the black patience stone of Persian mythology, that hears all, then shatters, leaving you delivered of pain and suffering.

Born in Afghanistan, **Atiq Rahimi** fled to France in 1984, where he has made a name as a writer, film and documentary maker. In the last ten years he has returned to Afghanistan many times, to set up a Writers' House in Kabul and offer support and training to young writers and film-makers. *The Patience Stone* won the 2008 Prix Goncourt.

Polly McLean's previous translations include biographies of Catherine Deneuve and Sylvia Kristel, *Lobster* by Guillaume Lecasble and the award-winning *Secret* by Philippe Grimbert. She won the 2009 Scott Moncrieff prize for *Gross Margin* by Laurent Quintreau.

The dove flyer

Although we should have been sleeping on the roof as we always did during the summer in Baghdad, my mother had yet to bring up the beds, fit them with mosquito netting, and put the water jug out to cool on the balcony. Perhaps she was loath to acknowledge the change of the seasons or feared the late spring sandstorms that turned the city's skies red.

My father saw storm warnings too, which had raged like a whirling sword since the hanging of the wealthy Jewish merchant Shafik Addas. Every night the CID, the Iraqi secret service, visited houses in search of weapons, two-way radios, and the Hebrew textbooks distributed by 'the Movement', as the Zionist underground was called by us. Hundreds of Jews were dragged off to torture chambers and forced to confess at summary trials staged by the military regime.

Shafik Addas was not a native Iraqi. He was a Syrian who had turned up one day in Basra, the City of Date Palms, and gone into the car import business from which he made a fortune put at millions of dinars. Among the regular guests in his mansion were wazirs, emirs, sheikhs, army officers, even Regent Abdullah. Addas was to Basra what Big Imari, my father's cousin, was to Baghdad. It was his overconfidence that proved his downfall. Instead of taking – like Big Imari – a Moslem from a prominent family to manage his affairs, deal with government officials and bribe them when necessary, he ran his business himself and acted the equal of any Arab. He was envied and made enemies, and neither his aloofness from his fellow Jews nor the life of a dyed-in-the-wool Iraqi that he led were able to save him in the end.

A hot desert wind blew that night. Lying in the *kabishkan*, my little attic room, I couldn't fall asleep. It was asphyxiatingly hot and I was worried. Worse yet, Miss Sylvia had picked the next day to test us on Hamlet's 'To be or not to be' and I wanted badly to outperform George. *To be or not to be*. What choice was there? I was too young to dwell on death but the fate of Shafik Addas kept me awake. One spin of fortune's wheel and even a *muhtashem* like him, a potentate at the height of his career, was just another Jew at the end of a rope. Although I hadn't seen it, I could picture the screaming mob in the square. Both old Hiyawi and my Uncle Hizkel had been there and told me about it.

It had happened less than a year before, right after Passover, during the wave of arrests that followed the establishment of Israel. The new defence minister Sadik al-Bassam, or Sadik el-Bassam Damn-His-Soul as we Jews called him, had wanted to teach us a lesson. Shafik Addas was a godsend. The editor of the Basra newspaper *An-Nas* had asked him for a 'contribution' of a thousand dinars and Addas had refused to comply. What, he had thought, could a mere journalist do to him when he was friends with everyone in the government and police?

Now, lying in bed, I couldn't help reflecting how the choice of whether to be or not to be was sometimes made without knowing. Two days later the editor published a vicious article accusing Addas of selling arms to 'the Zionist gangs' and spying for *ad-dowa al maz'uma*, 'the make-believe state', as Israel was called. The newspaper demanded an investigation, and as soon as copies of it reached Baghdad there was a clamour for Addas's head. It was practically a holy war; the whole country talked of nothing else. The only one who seemed unaffected was Addas himself, who – or so it now seemed – had lost his instinct for survival. The night before his arrest he was secretly visited by the provincial governor, Fahri el-Tabakchali, who urged him to flee to Iran in a speedboat that was waiting to take him safely across the Shatt-el-Arab and out of danger in half an hour. Addas wouldn't hear of it. 'They have nothing on me,' he insisted each time the governor quoted the proverb *El-hazima ranima*, 'He who runs for his life takes it with him as his loot.'

The next day Addas was arrested. The trial lasted three days. His three lawyers resigned one by one because the judge, Abdallah en-Na'san, a Jew-hating army officer, refused to hear any defence witnesses. Sadik al-Bassam signed the death warrant at once, after which the Regent equivocated for three days. He was Addas's friend and knew better than anyone what a patriot the condemned man had been. Yet when Addas's wife went down on her knees before him, he could only stare at the ground and reply that the matter was no longer in his hands.

'Kabi, my boy,' said old Hiyawi, 'what can I tell you? The day before the execution I went to Basra with your Uncle Hizkel to fast and pray with the Jews there as Rabbi Bashi told us to do. On the way I wanted to say a prayer at the tomb of the prophet Ezekiel in Kifl. I was afraid your uncle would refuse – you know what a firebrand he is – but he not only agreed, he said he had been thinking of it too. By the time we reached Basra there were mass demonstrations in the streets. Even small children were carrying effigies of Addas and calling for his blood. And the next day – woe to the eyes that saw it! – he was hanged in front of his home. Once wasn't enough for them; they actually strung him up twice. I'm an old man and I've never seen or heard the likes of it. The mob went as wild as if the prophet Muhammed had come back to life. There were thousands of Moslems from Basra and the area, and some who had come all the way from Baghdad. Whole families. They waited up all night, dancing and shouting *Allah akbar*. We were afraid to go out and watched through the cracks in the shutters. Kabi, what can I tell you? We live in a country where judges mock justice and rulers know no mercy.'

In their hotel that night he and my uncle didn't sleep a wink. Hizkel, from whom I heard the story too, said that Addas's trial reminded him of the Dreyfus Affair, which had inspired Herzl to write his book *The Jewish State*. My uncle was a passionate believer in Zionism and an expert on its history. After Addas's death he wrote an editorial titled 'Confessions Of The Hangman's Noose' for which the newspaper he published was shut down. 'The trial of Shafik Addas,' it said, 'was the trial of every Jew. If an Addas can be hanged, who will save the rest of us?'

I tossed and turned on my wooden bed until I felt as if I was rocking in a hammock. I dreamed of purple fields and of a great eagle that carried me to the fabled gates of Jerusalem and knocked on them with its beak. And then, all at once, I knew for a terrifying fact that the knocks were on our front gate. It was useless to try to ignore them by pulling the blanket over my head. I got out of bed and stared blindly into the dark. *They're here*. They would find the arms. They would take my father.

I roused myself and went downstairs to my parents' room. The light was on and my mother stood by the double bed with the colour gone from her face. My father lay in bed. He had been running a fever for three days and had dark bags beneath his bloodshot eyes. Strands of thick grey hair stuck out from his woollen cap and his thin moustache had all but vanished in his unshaven face.

'They're here!' whispered my mother in an unsteady voice.

'What will we do, Abu Kabi?'

'Kabi, open the gate for them,' said my father.

I headed for the courtyard, stopping at the end of the long hallway to grope for the light switch. My breath came in shallow spurts. The banging on the gate made me tremble. 'I'm coming, I'm coming,' I tried calling in Moslem Arabic, but the words came out in a Jewish dialect. I turned the big key and lifted the heavy wooden latch that my Uncle Hizkel had made not long before. I was immediately pinned against the wall. Four soldiers burst inside, dragging Hizkel who lived nearby. His bloody face was beaten to a pulp. His wife Rashel followed frantically behind them.

'Look what they've done to him!' she wailed.

'He'll swing for it,' said a soldier, running a finger over his throat.

'No!' She let out a scream and reached for Hizkel, clutching at his shoulder.

'Out of the way, you!' barked the soldier.

The devastation lasted a good hour-and-a-half. At four in the morning I was back in the courtyard again, accompanying the soldiers to the gate. Hizkel was lying by the cesspit. He seemed to be trying to smile at me with his swollen lips that were mashed out of shape. Rashel sat beside him with a frightened look, stroking his wounds as if drawing the pain from them. One of the soldiers, named Adnan, was in a vile mood because an oil lamp had shattered in his hands while he was searching the cellar. He rammed the *jalala*, the wooden chair-swing, with his rifle butt until it split lengthwise and calmed down only after booting Hizkel in the ribs. Rashel tried desperately to shield him and was driven back with a blow to her chest. Her eyes filled with tears.

Adnan studied the oil stain on his uniform. I wanted to throw a lit match at it. Would I ever carry out any of my fantasies? Not until the day that I could overcome my fear of these soldiers.

An officer appeared in the courtyard and ordered that Hizkel be taken away. Before he could get to his feet he was dragged to a jeep outside, his eyes two white flares in the dark lane.

'*Kus um-el-yahud*, get the hell up!' yelled Adnan.

Hizkel tried raising himself with his handcuffed arms, collapsed, and tried again. In the end he got to his feet with Rashel's help. He stiffened when he saw me, turning his head away from the soldiers to hide a grimace that seemed to say: *Hush not a word you know nothing*. Perhaps Rashel, who was not in on the secret, was not meant to see either. She supported him while Adnan eyed her trim body in the glare of the headlights.

'Instead of messing around with these Jews, we ought to be fucking their wives,' he said.

'Watch it now,' said the officer with a wag of his finger as he climbed into the jeep by the driver. 'Allah let you off easy this time.' Two soldiers pushed Hizkel into the back seat and sat on either side of him.

'Hizkel, Hizkel,' wept Rashel. The jeep disappeared around a curve in the lane, leaving behind a stench of exhaust.

From *The Dove Flyer* by **Eli Amir**, translated from the Hebrew by
Hillel Halkin (Halban 2010)

In 1950, each member of Kabi's Jewish circle in Baghdad has a different
dream. His mother wants to return to the Moslem quarter where she felt
safer; his father wants to emigrate to Israel and grow rice; Salim, his
headmaster, wants Arabs and Jews to be equal, and Abu Edouard wants to
be left alone to care for his adored doves. But his Uncle Hizkel's arrest is the
beginning of a perilous future. *The Dove Flyer* reconstructs in moving detail
the decline and persecution of another Middle Eastern minority, the
centuries-old Jewish community of Baghdad.

    Eli Amir was born in Baghdad, and his family moved to Israel in 1951.
He served as special advisor to the Prime Minister, responsible for Arab
affairs in east Jerusalem, and worked as a political columnist, lecturer, and
member of the Israeli delegation on Palestinian refugee affairs. Currently
Amir is chairman of the public council of The Abraham Fund for
Coexistence and Equality between Israeli Arabs and Jews. His work has
received many awards.

Hillel Halkin has lived in Israel since 1970, working as a translator,
journalist, and author. A leading Hebrew-English and Yiddish-English
translator, he has translated more than fifty works of fiction, poetry, and
drama, including classic works by Agnon, Sholem Aleichem, Y. L. Peretz,
and contemporary Israeli writers such as Amos Oz and A.B. Yehoshua. As a
journalist, Halkin was nominated for a Pulitzer Prize when he wrote for the
New York weekly *Forward*, and he has written widely on Israeli and Jewish
politics, literature and culture.

Dreams in a time of war

Years later when I read T. S. Eliot's line that April was the cruellest month, I would recall what happened to me one April day in 1954, in chilly Limuru, the prime estate of what, in 1902, another Eliot, Sir Charles Eliot, then governor of colonial Kenya, had set aside as White Highlands. The day came back to me, the now of it, vividly.

I had not had lunch that day, and my tummy had forgotten the porridge I had gobbled that morning before the six-mile run to Kīnyogori Intermediate School. Now there were the same miles to cross on my way back home; I tried not to look too far ahead to a morsel that night. My mother was pretty good at conjuring up a meal a day, but when one is hungry, it is better to find something, anything, to take one's mind away from thoughts of food. It was what I often did at lunchtime when other kids took out the food they had brought and those who dwelt in the neighborhood went home to eat during the midday break. I would often pretend that I was going someplace, but really it was to any shade of a tree or cover of a bush, far from the other kids, just to read a book, any book, not that there were many of them, but even class notes were a welcome distraction. That day I read from the abridged version of Dickens's *Oliver Twist*. There was a line drawing of Oliver Twist, a bowl in hand, looking up to a towering figure, with the caption 'Please sir, can I have some more?' I identified with that question; only for me it was often directed at my mother, my sole benefactor, who always gave more whenever she could.

Listening to stories and anecdotes from the other kids was also a soothing distraction, especially during the walk back home, a lesser ordeal than in the morning when we had to run barefoot to school, all the way, sweat streaming down our cheeks, to avoid tardiness and the inevitable lashes on our open palms. On the way home, except for those kids from Ndeiya or Ngeca who had to cover ten miles or more, the walk was more leisurely. It was actually better so, killing time on the road before the evening meal of uncertain regularity or chores in and around the home compound.

Kenneth, my classmate, and I used to be quite good at killing time, especially as we climbed the last hill before home. Facing the sloping side, we each would kick a 'ball', mostly Sodom apples, backward over our heads up the hill. The next kick would be from where the first ball had landed, and so on, competing to beat each other to the top. It was not the easiest or fastest way of getting there, but it had the virtue of making us forget the world. But now we were too big for that kind of play. Besides, no games could beat storytelling for capturing our attention.

We often crowded around whoever was telling a tale, and those who were really good at it became heroes of the moment. Sometimes, in competing for proximity to the narrator, one group would push him off the main path to one side; the other group would shove him back to the other side, the entire lot zigzagging along like sheep.

This evening was no different, except for the route we took. From Kīnyogori to my home village, Kwangūgī or Ngamba, and its neighborhoods we normally took a path that went through a series of ridges and valleys, but when listening to a tale, one did not notice the ridge and fields of corn, potatoes, peas, and beans, each field bounded by wattle trees or hedges of kei apple and gray thorny bushes. The path eventually led to the Kīhingo area, past my old elementary school, Manguo, down the valley, and then up a hill of grass and black wattle trees. But today, following, like sheep, the lead teller of tales, we took another route, slightly longer, along the fence of the Limuru Bata Shoe factory, past its stinking dump site of rubber debris and rotting hides and skins, to a junction of railway tracks and roads, one of which led to the marketplace. At the crossroads was a crowd of men and women, probably coming from market, in animated discussion. The crowd grew larger as workers from the shoe factory also stopped and joined in. One or two boys recognized some relatives in the crowd. I followed them, to listen.

'He was caught red-handed,' some were saying.

'Imagine, bullets in his hands. In broad daylight.'

Everybody, even we children, knew that for an African to be caught with bullets or empty shells was treason; he would be dubbed a terrorist, and his hanging by the rope was the only outcome.

'We could hear gunfire,' some were saying.

'I saw them shoot at him with my own eyes.'

'But he didn't die!'

'Die? Hmm! Bullets flew at those who were shooting.'

'No, he flew into the sky and disappeared in the clouds.'

Disagreements among the storytellers broke the crowd into smaller groups of threes, fours, and fives around a narrator with his own perspective on what had taken place that afternoon. I found myself moving from one group to another, gleaning bits here and there. Gradually I pieced together strands of the story, and a narrative of what bound the crowd emerged, a riveting tale about a nameless man who had been arrested near the Indian shops. The shops were built on the ridge, rows of buildings that faced each other, making for a huge rectangular enclosure for carriages and shoppers, with entrance-exits at the corners. The ridge sloped down to a plain where stood African-owned buildings, again built to form a similar rectangle, the enclosed space often used as a market on Wednesdays and Saturdays. The goats and sheep for sale on the same two market days were tethered in groups in the large sloping space between the two sets of shopping centres. That area had apparently been the theatre of action that now animated the group of narrators and listeners. They all agreed that after handcuffing the man, the police put him in the back of their truck.

Suddenly, the man had jumped out and run. Caught unawares, the police turned the truck around and chased the man, their guns aimed at him. Some of them jumped out and pursued him on foot. He mingled with shoppers and then ran through a gap between two shops into the open space between the Indian and African shops. Here, the police opened fire. The man would fall, but only to rise again and run from side to side. Time and again this had happened, ending only with the man's zigzagging his way through the herds of sheep and goats, down the slopes, past the African shops, across the rails, to the other side, past the crowded workers' quarters of the Limuru Bata Shoe Company, up the ridge till he disappeared, apparently unharmed, into the European-owned lush green tea plantations. The chase had turned the hunted, a man without a name, into an instant legend, inspiring numerous tales of heroism and magic among those who had witnessed the event and others who had received the story secondhand.

I had heard similar stories about Mau Mau guerrilla fighters, Dedan Kĩmathi in particular; only, until then, the magic had happened far away in Nyandarwa and the Mount Kenya mountains, and the tales were never told by anybody who had been an eyewitness. Even my friend Ngandi, the most informed teller of tales, never said that he had actually seen any of the actions he described so graphically. I love listening more than telling, but this was the one story I was eager to tell, before or after the meal. Next time I met Ngandi, I could maybe hold my own.

The X-shaped barriers to the railway crossing level were raised. A siren sounded, and the train passed by, a reminder to the crowd that they still had miles to go. Kenneth and I followed suit, and when no longer in the company of the other students he spoiled the mood by contesting the veracity of the story, at least the manner in which it had been told. Kenneth liked a clear line between fact and fiction; he did not relish the two mixed. Near his place, we parted without having agreed on the degree of exaggeration.

Home at last, to my mother, Wanjikũ, and my younger brother, Njinjũ, my sister Njoki, and my elder brother's wife, Charity. They were huddled together around the fireside. Despite Kenneth, I was still giddy with the story of the man without a name, like one of those characters in books. Sudden pangs of hunger brought me back to earth. But it was past dusk, and that meant an evening meal might soon be served.

Food was ready all right, handed to me in a calabash bowl, in total silence. Even my younger brother, who liked to call out my failings, such as my coming home after dusk, was quiet. I wanted to explain why I was late, but first I had to quell the rumbling in my tummy.

In the end, my explanation was not necessary. My mother broke the silence. Wallace Mwangi, my elder brother, Good Wallace as he was popularly known, had earlier that afternoon narrowly escaped death. We pray for his safety in the mountains. It is this war, she said.

—

From *Dreams in a Time of War* by **Ngũgĩ wa Thiong'o**, translated by the author (Harvill Secker 2010)

Beginning in the late 1930s, Ngũgĩ wa Thiong'o's memoir describes his day-to-day life as the fifth child of his father's third wife in a family that included twenty-four children born to four different mothers. Against the backdrop of World War II, which affected the lives of Africans under British colonial rule in unexpected ways, Ngũgĩ attended school to satisfy what was considered a bizarre thirst for learning. Later, through the stories of his grandparents and parents and of brothers' involvement on different sides of the violent Mau Mau uprising, he recaptures a landscape, a culture and a people at profound moments of their history, under colonialism and war.

Ngũgĩ wa Thiong'o is Distinguished Professor of English and Comparative Literature at the University of California, Irvine, and is director of the university's International Centre for Writing and Translation. His books include *Petals of Blood*, for which he was imprisoned by the Kenyan government in 1977, and *Wizard of the Crow*, which was published by Harvill Secker to great acclaim in 2006.

Small talk in shades of white

Look I'm getting annoyed now. If you carry on like this, I'm off. You want to know what you've done wrong? Why am I not surprised? For one thing, the way you're sitting and staring at me is winding me up. You're playing at being quiet and considerate, hoping that I take you for a civilised, intelligent man. Well, we're not in a mosque now. We're in a bar. And you're really getting on my nerves. Even that smile plastered across your lips so you come across all smart and reasonable. I find it really offensive. Do you really think you're that clever? And the other people here are shallow types who can only make small talk? No, darling, you're wrong. Shall I tell you what's going on in your head? You're playing at being clever, but you're not thinking clever. You've told yourself: 'This is just another slut. She looks drunk – brilliant. I'll only have to buy two beers and then I can invite her back to my place. She'll probably be tired and badly in need of sleep. Just sleep. When we get home, I won't ask her if she's had dinner. I'll take her straight to the bedroom. We'll turn off the light, and we'll sleep. Once I've had had my way with her, I'll turn my back. And then, as usual, I'll snore all the way to the morning.' Open your eyes, my friend. Seems like you've fallen asleep right here in the bar. Do you really think you've got it all worked out? God help you. Has it occurred to you, even as a minor possibility, that the woman sat next to you is not a slut? And that she's only drinking like this because of the pain she feels, and that she badly needs a man of substance, who can have a deep conversation and listen, really listen to her. Maybe that's why she started talking to you. But even if I was out on the pull, what's stopping me from thinking like you? You're just a filthy drunk. I can down a few glasses at your expense and then give you the slip. And let's suppose I did go back to your place with you. Who's to say that I won't be the one to turn my back on you after sex? Why can't I be the one to get what I want and then slam the door behind me in the morning as I head out to get some more somewhere else, while you're the one who stays behind to make the bed, wash the sheets, and rub off the gunk that stuck on to you while you lay back and closed your eyes in the hope of bringing back some of the heat from the night's passion? Now who's the slut, you or me? Oh my God, are you still smiling at me like I'm telling a joke? You really are unbearable. Do you know what annoys me about men? It's that lack of sensitivity which gives them a superhuman ability to look at peace with themselves. You could sit there like you're not bothered, even if your insides were on fire. Take you, for example. You look around you in the bar like it's a strange and foreign land. The whores, the drunks, the shouting, the arguments – a madhouse. But you forget that you're here, slap bang in the middle of the madhouse. You've forgotten, haven't you? You think you're some kind of king and these others are a troupe of actors performing in your honour. If you're rubbing shoulders with them, it's only because you've come down off your throne and stepped on to the stage. No, darling. You've got it wrong. The basic difference between you and me is that I actually consider myself part of this race of lowlifes. I know that I am in a stinking bar. And when I leave at the end of the night, I'm going to have to watch my step, because the likes of you feel no shame in throwing up everywhere, hurling the beer that was festering in their guts out on to the counter or in the entrance, without anyone blinking an eye. Sometimes they throw up into the laps of their lady companions, forgetting that just a few moments ago they were respectable gentlemen. I'm not claiming to be respectable. I'm just a slut. But of course you're no better than me. You're as loose as I am. You walked into this dump to fill up on cheap beer and take a random woman home to your bed. Can you see how we're both the same when it comes to being worthless scum?

That's not to say that everyone here is a good-for-nothing. In this bar, I've met some real men. And they know what it means to be a man. Like that old fellow there – do you see him? – in the light brown overcoat, sitting by himself at the far end of the counter. No, that one there, behind Fateeha, the blonde. Ah, so you're not a real boozer – who here doesn't know him? His name is Saif Al-Mansouri, and he's worked since forever at the National Cooperative Bank. He's from Marrakesh, like you. He came to this city in the seventies and settled here for good. He's here every day, bless him. I've known him for years, and he's really sweet to me. Looks like he hasn't seen me. Mister Saif... Mister Saif... He didn't hear me. He once said to me that he prefers the noises of the bar to small talk. He can't stand talk, whether it's on the TV, from his wife or his kids. At least here he can lose himself in the noise and no one bothers him. Poor thing. If you knew how much he suffers. When he caught tuberculosis, everyone started avoiding him. He once said to me that even his wife kept her distance from him when they were in bed. Some of the really mean regulars gave him a nickname – Unsafe Al-Cansouri. The man's sick and the scumbags make fun of him. It's not the illness that he resents, it's people. Last Saturday, he told me that he had come to an understanding with the bugs that had built a home in his lungs, and then he said: 'But those turds would rather carry on talking about me behind my back. If I've got TB, it's my chest that's infected, it's me that's got to breathe with these lungs, not them, or their mothers. What can I do to look after my body at this age? I'm sixty-nine years old. I'm just dragging myself along, and I'm dragging all my years behind me as I splutter like an old train. I can tell you this, my love, there's nothing I'll regret more than dying while there's still one part of my body that's healthy. I'd rather break down gradually than burn out all of a sudden like a TV that's had a power surge.'

I can tell you, he really is a different sort of person. This one time, six years ago, he came out drinking with us at the Seven Dunes pub. He'd drunk a little too much, and I didn't want to leave him in the bar like that so I took him home with me. In those days, I used to live with Samia from Rabat – do you know her? – and this other girl who emigrated to Italy and got married there. The disease hadn't hit him yet. I won't lie to you, we used to find him very attractive then. Once inside, I took him to my room. I pushed him gently on to the bed and lay down next to him.

Seriously, I never feel quite myself except when I take my clothes off. I didn't hold back. I just had my underwear on. I embraced him tightly against my chest. Did I really want him that night? I don't know. But I hugged him close and rained kisses on his face. When I began to unbutton his shirt, he whispered into my ears in a tired voice: 'No Hajeeba. You are like a daughter to me…' My body started shaking and I burst into tears. He had never cheated on his wife. That's what he told me afterwards. And there was me, a slut. I was just a slut. Crying was not going to help me at that moment. I got out of bed and I began to get dressed, but he opened his eyes, and looked at me:

'Stay as you are, Hajeeba,' he said to me, 'and come sleep next to me. I will hold you like a father; put your head on my chest and sleep. I love your white underwear. White is a noble colour, my pet. So come and sleep in my arms, safe and sound.'

Since that night, I have always worn white underwear. White really is a noble colour. Look at the people on religious holidays, what are they wearing? White clothes. At the Friday prayer, worshippers wear white robes. The dead are wrapped in white shrouds. At weddings, they wear white. In mourning, it's white. As for you… Are you still smiling?! What's that now you cheeky sod? You want to check the colour of my bra for yourself? Then cough up the price of beer, you cheapskate. Don't worry about dinner. I'll treat you to a light meal at the Travellers' Diner. Tonight, I'll make you regret smiling like that. I'll light a fire inside your body and I'll make every part of it scream. Get up then. Oh, Mister Saif! Mister Saif... Enjoying your drink...? How are things...? No... Sorry, dear... I have a friend for tonight. I'm going now. Bye bye... Yes, tomorrow, of course... Of course... Of course...

Ouarzazate, April 1998

—

From '*Two Stories*' by **Yassin Adnan,** translated from the Arabic by Haroon Shirwani in Beirut39: New Writing From the Arab World edited by Samuel Shimon (Bloomsbury 2010)

Beirut39 presents young Arab writers from around the world. From Saudi Arabia to Morocco, from France to Syria and from Lebanon to the Netherlands and USA, and including short stories, extracts from novels, and poetry, the selection showcases a literature, or literatures, that have not been widely represented in the English-speaking world until now.

The judges who selected the 39 writers from almost five hundred candidates were Egyptian literary critic, Gaber Asfour; Lebanese poet and cultural editor of the international daily Al-Hayat newspaper, Abdo Wazen; Lebanese writer, Alawiya Sobh; and Omani poet and editor-in-chief of the Omani cultural magazine Nazwa, Saif al-Rahbi. The editor of *Beirut39*, Samuel Shimon, is an Iraqi writer and the editor of Banipal, the London-based magazine of new Arab writing in English translation.

Yassin Adnan is a Moroccan writer who has published three books of poetry and two collections of short stories, *Man yusaddiq al-rasa'il?* and *Tuffah al-zill*. He is the recipient of the Moufdi Zakaria Prize (Algeria, 1991), the Union of Writers in Morocco Poetry Prize (1998) and the Buland al-Haydari Prize for Young Poets (Asilah, 2003).

Haroon Shirwani is Head of Arabic at Eton College. He studied Arabic, French and History at Oxford and London universities. Each year he produces *A Taste of Texts* – a selection from Arabic literature with his translations – for use by students and teachers.

Afterword

Way back in Summer 2003, a meeting took place between then English PEN Director Susie Nicklin; the Director of Serpent's Tail Books, Pete Ayrton; and myself, then employed as the Arts Council's International Literature Officer. Over scrambled eggs at a greasy spoon on London's Kentish Town Road (opposite the former inglorious English PEN offices) we thrashed out a wish list as to how and where we'd like to see translation placed on the PEN agenda.

Two basic points could be held as self-evident. One was that, despite the understandable tendency for confusion with International PEN (which just happened also to have been founded in London and coordinates a major overseas network), English PEN had always worked internationally. Its Writers in Prison Committee, now 50 years old, makes regular visits to jailed authors in every region of the world and its London base organises actions here on their behalf. Therefore it made no sense not to be offering clear and concrete support for the publishing and publicising of these repressed writers' works in the language of English PEN.

The other point is that, simply, the rest of the world now wants to be translated into English. This is not simply because it is a dominant language – more people, after all, speak Mandarin – but because it is so widely diffused. It is also, increasingly, the language of global publishing, as more people both read and study in English.

Allied to both these facts is that when a book is banned in its country of origin it often circulates in a form of *samizdat*. One part of the new Writers in Translation committee's work would become the translation of samples from these unpublished (and, domestically, unpublishable) books, with a view to finding a British outlet. Equally – and this was unforeseen by the committee at first – such books could, if published in English, circulate in English versions in the country of origin. This was never more true than in the case of Writers in Translation's first choice of book to support, the late Anna Politkovskaya's *Putin's Russia*. Her account was unavailable in Russian, and thousands of English-language copies were surreptitiously, often bravely, circulated where they were most urgently needed to be read: inside Russia.

English PEN's remit, from its foundation in 1921, has been to give voice to the voiceless. The problem with publishing literary translations in Britain is not just that they amount to no more than three or four per cent of the colossal output of approximately 150,000 books published here annually, but that they tend to get so little critical and media attention. The second part of Writers in Translation's work was therefore to be the promotion of these books through the award of grants to publishers to hold public events to showcase these important books. As much, arguably, as financial support, the 'Recommended by PEN' logo on a book's cover helps to highlight the relevance of the books we supported to the aims of PEN and to the growing constituency of readers who care passionately about them.

In this, Writers in Translation has been conspicuously successful. It has brought new and old funding agencies together (Bloomberg and the Arts Council, London). It has allowed both small and large publishing houses with translation lists to appear together in important promotions. It has also raised the profile of authors at risk, allowing where necessary for other PEN committees and interested parties to take campaigning forward on their behalf. Writers in Translation may be the baby among these committees, but it continues to play a vital part in extending and publicising the work of the rest.

—

Amanda Hopkinson, Professor of Literary Translation, Senior Fellow in the School of Literature & Creative Writing at the University of East Anglia, and founding chair of the Writers in Translation committee

Acknowledgements

This anthology is dedicated to the memory of **Paul Marsh**.

Paul Marsh read English at Peterhouse College, Cambridge before joining Anthony Sheil Associates in 1977 - the start of a stellar career as one of the most respected international literary agents of his time. Fluent in French, German and Italian, Paul's understated, modest approach was nonetheless highly effective at facilitating the translation of literature into numerous other languages. Paul's eponymous agency, founded in 1994 with Susanna Nicklin, excelled at creating international publishing deals for writers such as Ben Okri, Arundhati Roy and Vikram Seth.

Paul not only understood the ability of translation to take great writing to readers of other languages around the world but he possessed the judgement, pragmatism and eye for a good book that earned him the trust, respect and friendship of so many authors and publishers around the world. Paul was always supportive of English PEN's Writers in Translation programme - not least, I suspect, because he understood that it was often well conceived, practical promotional activities that could make or break the international success of an author's work, however brilliantly it had been written, agented or translated.

Alistair Burtenshaw is Director, The London Book Fair

English PEN gratefully acknowledges the support of Arts Council England.

Every effort has been made to trace the copyright holders of all works included in this anthology. Any omission is unintentional, and the publisher would be happy to make due acknowledgement in future editions. Grateful acknowledgement is made to the following:

Introduction © Julian Evans, 2010

Anna Politkovskaya: extract from *Putin's Russia* © Anna Politkovskaya, 2004. Translation © Arch Tait, 2004. By kind permission of Random House UK Ltd.

Dubravka Ugresic: extract from *The Ministry of Pain* © Dubravka Ugresic, 2005. Translation © Michael Henry Heim, 2005. By kind permission of Telegram Books.

Jean Hatzfeld: extract from *Into the Quick of Life* © Éditions du Seuil, 2000. Translation © Gerry Feehily, 2005. By kind permission of Profile Books Ltd.

PEN's work is ongoing. To join us, please fill in the
membership form on the opposite page and send it to:
English PEN, Free Word Centre, 60 Farringdon Road,
London EC1R 3GA. Alternatively, visit www.englishpen.org

English PEN is a company limited by guarantee, number
5747142, and a registered charity, number 1125610

the reading agency

Supported by
**ARTS COUNCIL
ENGLAND**

English PEN

Membership Form

Payment is annual, by credit card, cheque or standing order. For further information please call 020 7324 2535 or visit www.englishpen.org.

Full name (in capitals):

Full address (in capitals):

Telephone:

Email:

I would like to join as (tick the appropriate box):

A Member (London & overseas) £50
B Member (outside London) £45
C Friend (London & overseas) £50
D Friend (outside London) £45
E Student £15

Please complete the standing order form opposite or send a cheque made payable to English PEN or this form with your card details completed to Free Word Centre, 60 Farringdon Road, London EC1R 3GA

Card number:

Expiry date:

Start date (if applicable):

Issue number (if applicable):

I would like to join the Rapid Action Network (please tick):

Standing Order Form

Full name and address of bank:

Please pay the account of English PEN, HSBC, Sloane Square Branch, 13-14 Sloane Square, London SW1W 8AL, Account No. 01129864, Sort code 40-06-15 from the following account:

Account name:

Account number:

Sort code:

The following amount (tick the appropriate box):

£50   £45   £15

Please take my first payment on (date):

/   /

and again on the same date annually until further notice.

Signature:

Date:

Gift Aid

Use Gift Aid and you can make your subscription worth more. For every pound you give to us, we get an extra 28 pence from the Inland Revenue. If you would like to Gift Aid your subscription and you are a registered tax payer just sign below:

I would like to make a donation to English PEN using Gift Aid.

giftaid it

Signature: